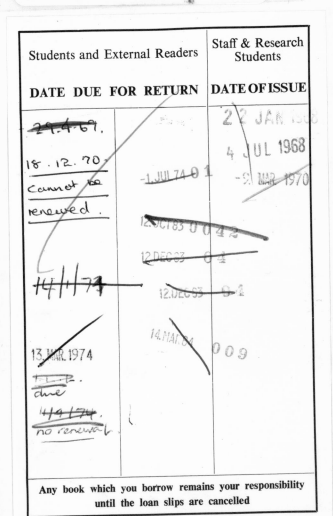

Students and External Readers	Staff & Research Students
DATE DUE FOR RETURN	**DATE OF ISSUE**

Students and External Readers — DATE DUE FOR RETURN:
- 29.4.69.
- 18.12.70
- Cannot be renewed.
- 14.1.74
- 13. MAR. 1974
- T.L.R. due
- 14.1.74. no renewal.

Staff & Research Students — DATE OF ISSUE:
- 2 2 JAN 1968
- 4 JUL 1968
- -1 JUL 74 0 1
- -9 MAR 1970
- 12. OCT 83 0 0 4 2
- 12 DEC 83 0 1
- 12. DEC 83 0 1
- 14. MAR 84 0 0 9

Any book which you borrow remains your responsibility until the loan slips are cancelled

THE METROPOLITAN
TRANSPORTATION SERIES

THE PERIPHERAL JOURNEY TO WORK

505630 .
Atch
NFG

The Peripheral Journey
to Work

A Geographic Consideration

Edward J. Taaffe
Barry J. Garner
Maurice H. Yeates

PUBLISHED FOR
THE TRANSPORTATION CENTER
AT NORTHWESTERN UNIVERSITY
BY NORTHWESTERN UNIVERSITY PRESS

FOREWORD

This study was initiated under the auspices of the Transportation Center at Northwestern University under a grant from the Automobile Manufacturers Association. The later portion of the study was aided by a National Science Foundation grant administered by Northwestern University. The authors would like to express their appreciation to these agencies and to the Chicago Area Transportation Study, which provided the basic data. Responsibility for the conclusions of the study and the manner in which the data were processed and interpreted rests solely with the authors.

TABLE OF CONTENTS

LIST OF TABLES

LIST OF FIGURES

THE PERIPHERAL JOURNEY TO WORK

CHAPTER I

Introduction

In modern urban geography, the study of the city's spatial organization has assumed a prominent role. Cities are viewed not only as static mosaics of different land uses but as dynamic, interdependent complexes of movement, orientations and traffic flow. The positioning of different bits of the mosaic with respect to each other becomes meaningful in a context of linkages and reciprocal spatial relationships. Any change in the broad pattern of metropolitan traffic flow may be taken both as a symptom of fundamental change in spatial organization, and as a force in itself, acting to bring about further changes in the locational strategy of the rest of the metropolitan area.

In this study, attention will be focused on one changing component of the aggregate metropolitan traffic flow, the journey-to-work to employment centers at the periphery of the city. As manufacturing continues to decentralize, the peripheral journey-to-work is becoming an ever more important component of the internal circulation system. A better understanding of the emerging character of peripheral laborsheds should, therefore, give some insight into the processes now changing the spatial organizational structure of American cities.

The nature of the peripheral journey-to-work also has significant implications for the extent of future metropolitan transportation problems. The relative concentration or dispersion of the peripheral laborsheds is a question of much importance. If the peripheral labor force is concentrated, it is possible that the daily journey-to-work will be shortened by continuing industrial decentralization. A series of separate work centers would then develop around the edge of the city, each with its own contiguous labor supply. On the other hand, peripheral firms may not be able to recruit nearby labor, and may be forced to draw on labor supplies in other parts of the metropolitan area. If the labor force is dispersed, the resultant cross-commuting currents from diverse origins to diverse destinations may aggravate, rather than alleviate, the congestion now associated with central business district commuting. The predominant mode of transportation of peripheral commuters is another important consideration. If there is a difference between central business district and peripheral commuters in the degree of importance of the private auto as opposed to mass transit, the nature and severity of the metropolitan traffic problem will be affected accordingly.

The objectives of this study are: (1) to identify key differences between the journey-to-work to peripheral centers, and to the central business district; (2) to develop a basic rationale for the observed peripheral commuting pattern in terms of distance, population distribution, and other relevant factors; (3) to speculate upon the implications of an anticipated increase in peripheral commuting for the spatial organization of the city.

Most of the study will be based on travel data gathered in 1956 by the Chicago Area Transportation Study. In particular, the data for a large district in the western suburbs of Chicago will be examined in detail. The district contains a considerable amount of new manufacturing and is felt to be reasonably representative of new manufacturing areas, developing in an essentially suburban context, just beyond the political limits of large American cities. Frequent reference will also be made to a selected group of studies touching, either explicitly or implicitly, on the peripheral journey-to-work in Chicago, New York and Boston. These include three studies of the impact of Boston's Route 128 (Burtt and M.I.T.); a portion of a major study of New York's industry (Hoover and Vernon); and a study of the decentralization of industry along Chicago's western sector (Reinemann).[1] The Burtt studies of Route 128 pro-

---

[1] Everett J. Burtt, Jr., *Labor Supply Characteristics of Route 128 Firms*, Research Report No. 1 (Boston: Federal Reserve Bank of Boston, 1958); Everett J. Burtt, Jr., *Changing Labor Supply Characteristics Along Route 128*, Research Report No. 17 (Boston: Federal Reserve Bank of Boston, 1961); *The Economic Impact of Massachusetts Route 128*, a report prepared by the Transportation Engineering Division and

vide a particularly useful complement. The present study is cross-sectional, since the travel data are confined to 1956, and aggregative, since firms are grouped by cells. Burtt's studies deal with changes through time and are based on interviews with individual firms.

In view of the diversity in usage of even the simple descriptive terms now prevalent in urban literature, the authors felt that it would be helpful to define briefly some of the terms used in this study to identify parts of the city. These are arbitrary terms identifying those parts of a metropolitan area which the authors feel to be well differentiated in terms of transportation, population and industrial characteristics. Figure I–1 is a diagrammatic representation of a metropolitan area. Within the city proper, there are three zones: the central business district or CBD; the fringe or frame of the CBD; and the large mass of the city, here referred to as the middle zone. There are three zones beyond the middle zone: the peripheral zone, and the radial and interstitial suburban zones. The peripheral zone is at the edge of the city, lying both inside and outside the city limits. Outlying shopping centers, belt railways and peripheral highways such as Boston's Route 128 are found in this zone, as is a considerable proportion of the new manufacturing development in metropolitan areas. The radial outer zones are aligned along major transportation axes, often including commuter railroads. They represent older suburban settlements and have good access to the CBD, considering their distance. The broad zones between the radials have been termed the interstitial areas. These are the new, auto-oriented suburbs, characterized by scattered subdivisions and low population densities. Our particular concern in this study will be with the commuting impact of the development of new industries in the peripheral zone. The out-migration of industry from points within the city to this zone is a metropolitan

Department of Civil and Sanitary Engineering at the Massachusetts Institute of Technology (Cambridge: Massachusetts Institute of Technology, December 31, 1958); E. M. Hoover and R. Vernon, *Anatomy of a Metropolis: The Changing Distribution of People and Jobs Within the New York Metropolitan Region* (Cambridge: Harvard University Press, 1959); Martin Reinemann, *The Localization and the Relocation of Manufacturing Within the Chicago Urban Area* (unpublished Ph.D. dissertation, Department of Geography, Northwestern University, 1955).

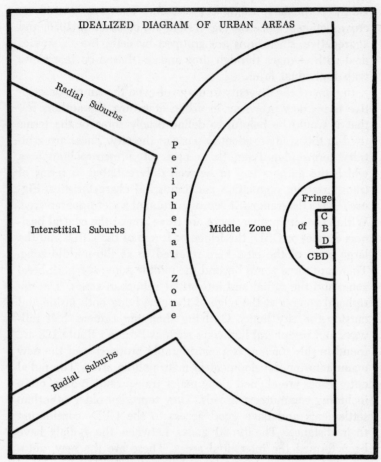

Idealized Diagram of Urban Areas

Figure I-1

trend of long standing. Evidence indicates that it will take place at an even more rapid pace in the future.

The study is organized, as follows:

(1) In Chapter II, the differences between peripheral and central business district labor forces in mode of travel, composition of labor force, and distance traveled are identified;

(2) In Chapter III, the spatial pattern of the peripheral labor-shed is examined for evidences of concentration and dispersion;

(3) In Chapter IV, a simple probability model is developed to describe the basic relation of peripheral commuting to population, distance and suburban location;

(4) In Chapter V, the relation of certain additional factors to peripheral commuting is discussed;

(5) In Chapter VI, the conclusions are summarized and discussed in conjunction with findings from other studies, in terms of the probable impact of peripheral commuting on the spatial organization of the city, and the future pattern of metropolitan traffic.

CHAPTER II

A Comparison of Peripheral and Central Business District Commuting Patterns

The journey-to-work to peripheral employment centers would not be worth studying as a separate component of the aggregate pattern of metropolitan traffic flow, if it did not differ in several significant respects from the journey-to-work to places of employment in the central business district. In this section of the study, therefore, the peripheral and the CBD commuting patterns will be compared in terms of the following characteristics: (1) the relative importance of the different modes of transportation; (2) differences in the sex, occupation and age composition of the labor forces; (3) differences in commuting distance.

Mode of Transportation

There is a striking contrast between the central business district and the peripheral labor forces in mode of transportation. As indicated on Table II–1, use of the private auto is overwhelmingly dominant among West Suburban commuters.[1] Ap-

[1] All the tabulations, unless otherwise indicated, are based on data collected in 1956 by the Chicago Area Transportation Study. The data for West Suburban commuters are based on a one-in-thirty sample of first work trips. The data for the CBD are based on a sub-sample of approximately one-in-nine from the basic one-in-thirty sample. Destination areas in the sub-sample are CATS Districts 01 and 11, thereby including part of the fringe of the CBD.

TABLE II-1

MODE OF COMMUTER TRANSPORTATION

Mode	CBD (per cent)	West Suburban (per cent)
Auto Driver	24.4	65.4
Auto Passenger	5.7	18.3
Railroad	16.6	0.7
Elevated-Subway	24.4	1.3
Bus	28.4	7.4
Walk to Work	—	6.2

Note: The mode taxi and at home are missing.

proximately 84 per cent of the West Suburban commuters drive, or are driven to work in private autos, as opposed to only 30 per cent of the CBD commuters. The high-capacity, off-street modes, such as the commuter railroads and the elevated-subway, are of negligible significance in commutation to the West Suburban district. Together they account for only 2 per cent of the peripheral commuters, as opposed to 40 per cent of the CBD commuters. The bus is the only form of mass transportation of any significance to the peripheral commuter, and it only accounts for 7 per cent, approximately as many as walk to work. The three forms of mass transportation taken together reveal the contrast between the two types of commuting patterns. Rail, elevated-subway and bus account for only 9 per cent of the suburban commuters as opposed to fully 70 per cent of the CBD commuters. If one were to consider peak-hour travel only, it is probable that the contrast would be even greater. Surveys taken in Chicago during the morning peak indicate that 87 per cent of the commuters use transit.[2] Other large Eastern cities show similar dependence on mass transit for CBD commuting. Wilfred Owen notes figures of 83 per cent for New York, and 64 per cent for Boston.[3] Auto-oriented cities, such as Los Angeles, report considerably lower figures, however (31 per cent). In the case of the peripheral commuter's concentration on the private auto, the Route 128 study

[2] Chicago Area Transportation Study, *Data Projections*, Volume II (Chicago: Chicago Area Transportation Study, July, 1960), p. 56.

[3] Wilfred Owen, *The Metropolitan Transportation Problem* (Washington: The Brookings Institution, 1956), Appendix Table 15, p. 280.

results were similar to those of the West Suburban sample.
Burtt found that approximately 92 per cent of the workers
either drove, or were auto passengers.[4] He also noted that, in
the case of relocated firms, public transportation percentages
dropped from 30 per cent to a negligible amount. An earlier
survey of commuters in New England indicated that 72 per
cent of the suburban workers used automobiles for their journey-to-work.[5]

The high auto-commuting figures are understandable when
the difficulties of commuting to the periphery by public transportation are considered. Reverse commuting by public
transportation from a nearby city area to a focal zone some-
where on the periphery presents particular difficulty. Public
transportation routes and schedules, as they have evolved in
major cities, are not designed to meet the needs of a reverse
commuting pattern. Typically the routes are markedly radial,
and focus on the CBD with no tendency for a similar focus
upon points at the edge of the city. This is particularly true of
the high-capacity, off-street forms of transportation such as the
elevated-subway and commuter railroads. Another difficulty is
the presence of the city boundary. Bus services and the extensions of elevated-subway service across such boundaries are
not easily accomplished. There is little incentive for the city
to develop services designed to ease the labor problems of
suburban firms, as opposed to city firms. Suburban commuters
from interstitial areas usually face similar problems. These
commuters are far away from elevated or commuter rail facilities, and are also faced with political barriers to through bus
service, because of the number of small separate suburbs. A
commuter from the adjacent suburban radial would seem to
face the fewest difficulties, because he would usually be able
to use the commuter railroads. Rail schedules are frequently
ill-adapted to his needs, however, and the newer peripheral
employment centers are frequently some distance from the
railroad station. In the West Suburban sample, less than 1 per

[4] Burtt, *Changing Labor Supply Characteristics Along Route 128*,
p. 45.

[5] Leonard P. Adams and Thomas W. Mackesey, *Commuting Patterns
of Industrial Workers, A Study of Experience in the Northeast Region*,
Research Publication No. 1 (Ithaca, New York: Housing Research Center, Cornell University, 1955), p. 88.

cent of all commuters were found to use the railroad, despite the fact that services are available to parts of the destination district. Political barriers also reduce the effectiveness of the bus connections between adjacent suburbs on the same radial, just as they do for interstitial suburbs. It seems unlikely that traffic and residential density in the future will be such as to permit the economic operation of rapid-transit facilities designed to bring workers into the peripheral employment centers. In the New York study, Hoover and Vernon note the failure of public transportation to increase with population growth in peripheral and outlying areas.[6] In both the Chicago and Boston examples, most of the areas are located beyond the effective range of the cities' rapid-transit systems, and the studies indicated that bus services were unsatisfactory. In both cities, examples are cited of individual plants developing chartered bus services on their own, and finding that little use was being made of them.

Table II–2 indicates that there are also important differences

TABLE II–2

MODE OF COMMUTER TRANSPORTATION BY SEX

	CBD		West Suburban	
	Male (per cent)	Female (per cent)	Male (per cent)	Female (per cent)
Auto Driver	36.9	4.7	77.4	26.6
Auto Passenger	4.6	8.6	11.6	39.9
Railroad	16.1	17.7	0.3	1.8
Elevated-Subway	20.1	31.9	1.0	2.2
Bus	21.9	36.9	5.0	15.1
Walk to Work	—	—	4.0	13.3

Note: The mode "taxi" and "at home" are missing.

between male and female commuters in mode of travel. Women are much more likely than men to walk to work, take the bus, or be auto passengers. Only 27 per cent of the women in the West suburban sample drive to work as compared to 77 per cent of the men. The greatest contrast is in auto passengers —40 per cent of all women commuters in the West Suburban

[6] Hoover and Vernon, *op. cit.,* p. 218.

district are auto passengers as opposed to only 12 per cent of
the men. The CBD commuters show similar contrasts between
male and female auto drivers. The female CBD commuters
are predominantly public transit passengers, however, rather
than auto passengers. More than two-thirds of the women ride
the bus or the elevated-subway. The higher percentage of
suburban women auto drivers may be an indication of a trend
toward increased auto-driving on the part of female commuters. On the other hand, it may merely be another reflection
of the absence of effective mass transit facilities in peripheral
commuting. Although no specific car pool information was
examined, there is some suggestion in the table that car pools
are most important among suburban female commuters. Evidence as to the overall difference between CBD and peripheral commuting in the importance of car pools must be regarded as inconclusive, however. The ratios between total car
occupants and drivers does not differ significantly between
CBD commuters (1.23) and peripheral commuters (1.27).

Composition of the Labor Force

In Tables II–3, II–4, and II–5, the CBD and West Suburban
labor forces are compared in terms of sex, occupational structure and age. The results of these comparisons indicate that
there are fewer women in the peripheral labor force, and that
a considerably higher percentage of the workers are in the
craftsmen and operators' category.

SEX

Table II–3 indicates the degree of difference between the
CBD and the periphery in the proportions of male and female
commuters. The female labor force drops from approximately

TABLE II–3

| | SEX OF COMMUTERS | |
Sex	CBD (per cent)	West Suburban (per cent)
Male	68	77
Female	32	23

one-third of the total in the CBD, to less than one-fourth in the periphery. This tendency for a lower percentage of female workers in peripheral employment centers was also cited in the Boston, New York and Chicago studies. It has proved difficult for peripheral firms to meet their needs both for female clerical and for female production workers. Reinemann's Chicago study indicated an even lower percentage than the West Suburban sample. He found that women constitute only 10 per cent of the labor force of manufacturing plants in the suburban portion of his Chicago traverse, as compared to over 25 per cent of the labor force in both the middle and the inner zones.[7]

Two reasons might be cited for the apparent reluctance of women to accept employment in the peripheral areas: the need for the private auto, and the absence of CBD amenities. Autos are not always available to female workers. Many of the young unmarried women do not own autos; many of the married women's husbands use the family car in their own commuting. There is also a wage factor in that low-cost public transportation would be expected to be an attractive alternate form of transportation for relatively low-wage female clerical workers. In addition to these fundamentally economic advantages of the CBD for women, most of the studies surveyed cited the importance of certain downtown amenities in slowing down the centrifugal migration of the female labor force. The central business district offers greater choice of restaurants, more variety in shopping and window-shopping, more cultural and recreational activities, and provides more opportunity to meet prospective husbands. The Route 128 study cited an example of a downtown firm which carefully recruited its female clerical help from the suburban area to which it was planning relocation. The attraction of downtown Boston proved to be so great, however, that, when the relocation was accomplished, many of the girls resigned and went to work for another downtown firm. The Boston studies also indicated that firms are finding it necessary to adopt a variety of recruitment policies to meet this problem. Burtt cites examples such as special appeals to housewives, finder's fees, and the use of five to eleven P.M. shifts.[8] Hoover and Vernon were more opti-

[7] Reinemann, op. cit., p. 98.

mistic in their New York studies as to the feasibility of peripheral employment centers meeting their female labor needs within the nearby suburban area. They felt that firms employing less than five hundred female office workers could decentralize without encountering labor force difficulties, and cited several instances of long automobile journeys-to-work by female employees.[9]

AGE AND OCCUPATION

Tables II–4 and II–5 indicate a contrast in occupational structure between the periphery and the central business

TABLE II–4

OCCUPATION OF COMMUTERS

Occupation	CBD (per cent)	West Suburban (per cent)
Professionals and Managers	24.5	18.7
Clerical Workers	30.9	15.4
Sales Workers	8.2	3.8
Craftsmen, Operatives and Laborers	28.7	55.7
Service Workers	7.7	6.4

TABLE II–5

AGE OF COMMUTERS

Age Group (years)	CBD (per cent)	West Suburban (per cent)
5–9	0.2	0.1
10–14	0.1	0.1
15–19	4.4	4.6
20–24	8.7	8.6
25–29	9.4	10.4
30–34	12.3	11.1
35–44	24.8	29.0
45–54	22.4	19.2
55–64	13.5	14.6
over 65	4.2	2.3

[8] Burtt, *Changing Labor Supply Characteristics Along Route 128*, p. 18.

[9] Hoover and Vernon, *op. cit.*, p. 103.

district, but little difference in age composition. Table II–4 shows that more than one-half of the West Suburban labor force is classed as craftsmen, operatives, or laborers, reflecting the greater emphasis on manufacturing in the peripheral zone. There are really three separate categories represented in this one grouping. Of these, the laborers form by far the smallest group—7 per cent, as opposed to 24 and 25 per cent, respectively, for craftsmen and operatives. This corresponds with the findings of other studies as to the scarcity of unskilled labor in peripheral districts. The larger percentage of professional and managerial workers in the CBD are a reflection of the lesser prevalence of manufacturing. It would not necessarily hold true, if the peripheral district were to be compared with manufacturing districts near the center of the city. Thus, statements in other studies to the effect that peripheral districts are ideal for the recruitment of professional and technical personnel are not necessarily contradicted by Table II–4.

In general, the age composition as shown in Table II–5 does not differ significantly between the two areas. If anything, the West Suburban labor force seems to be slightly younger. There are more workers in the 35–44 category, and fewer workers in the over 44 category. Further analyses and breakdown by occupational groups would be necessary, however, to bear out fully the statement, that the peripheral labor force tends to be younger than that of the CBD.

DISTANCE

A critical question is that of the average commuting distance for peripheral employment centers as compared to the central business district. If the average length of the peripheral journey-to-work is less than that to the CBD, then, all other things being equal, one might expect metropolitan traffic congestion to be alleviated by the continuing trend toward industrial decentralization, as discussed in Chapter I. An early study by Douglas Carroll indicated that, at least in the pre-war period, there was a marked tendency for the labor force in outlying centers to cluster around those centers.[10] Although the question was not treated in an explicitly spatial sense in the New York or Boston studies, it was generally observed that the maximum

[10] J. Douglas Carroll, Jr., "The Relation of Homes to Work Places and the Spatial Patterns of Cities," *Social Forces* (March, 1952), p. 272.

accessibility of the CBD resulted in a laborshed dispersed throughout the entire metropolitan area, whereas the peripheral centers tended to draw much of their labor force from nearby areas. The New York study indicated that suburb-to-suburb commuting in general was becoming more important. Three-fourths of the labor force of the inner ring of suburbs also lived in that inner ring.[11] In one of the Boston studies, it was noted that the average length of the journey-to-work decreased as plants moved from central Boston to Route 128 locations. In Reinemann's Chicago traverse, the commuting pattern of a firm located on the fringe of the CBD was compared with that of a peripheral firm.[12] The CBD firm's labor force was widely dispersed along mass transit and railroad radials; the peripheral firm's was less widely dispersed and showed no commuters from the more distant sections of the city. In the West Suburban sample there is a clear contrast to the central business district. The average distance traveled by peripheral commuters is 5.23 miles as compared to 6.72 miles for the CBD. The differences between the two are presented in more detail in Table II–6, however, where the percentage

TABLE II–6

COMMUTING DISTANCE

Distance Traveled (miles)	CBD (per cent)	West Suburban (per cent)
0– .9	1.94	18.89
1.0– 1.9	5.13	16.10
2.0– 2.9	6.71	10.97
3.0– 3.9	8.54	7.57
4.0– 4.9	9.45	6.70
5.0– 5.9	9.24	6.35
6.0– 6.9	9.51	6.35
7.0– 7.9	10.42	4.70
8.0– 8.9	9.99	4.96
9.0– 9.9	6.37	3.92
10.0–10.9	4.54	4.09
11.0–11.9	3.03	3.57
12.0–12.9	2.00	1.13
13.0–13.9	3.03	1.57
over 14.0	10.10	3.13

[11] Hoover and Vernon, *op. cit.*, p. 145.
[12] Reinemann, *op. cit.*, pp. 100–105.

distribution of commuters by distance traveled, is given. This
distribution is also presented graphically in Figure II–1. The
peripheral curve drops off steeply from its highest position

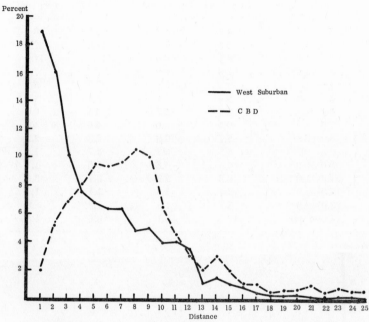

Distance Profiles—CBD and West Suburban Commuters

Figure II–1

within the first two miles of commuting distance. The CBD
curve starts from a low inside the first mile to an irregular
plateau between four and nine miles from the center. Median-
mile figures indicate that a commuting distance of 3.5 miles
includes one-half of the West Suburban commuters, as compared to 6.8 miles for one-half of the CBD commuters.

Distances traveled by male and female commuters indicate
some interesting differences. The West Suburban analysis
shows that females traveled an average of 3.48 miles, as compared to 5.23 miles for male commuters. In the CBD, the
average trip for female commuters was actually slightly longer
than that for male commuters: 7.13 miles as compared to 6.72
miles. This contrast is more evident in Table II–7 and Figures

TABLE II–7

COMMUTING DISTANCE BY SEX

Distance Traveled (miles)	CBD		West Suburban	
	Male (per cent)	Female (per cent)	Male (per cent)	Female (per cent)
0 – .9	2.4	1.2	15.9	28.7
1.0– 1.9	5.5	4.5	14.3	22.0
2.0– 2.9	6.7	6.6	10.7	11.9
3.0– 3.9	7.8	10.0	7.7	7.1
4.0– 4.9	9.3	9.8	7.2	5.2
5.0– 5.9	8.9	10.1	7.4	3.0
6.0– 6.9	8.2	11.7	6.5	6.0
7.0– 7.9	9.5	12.0	4.6	4.9
8.0– 8.9	8.7	12.3	5.8	2.2
9.0– 9.9	6.7	5.7	4.7	1.5
10.0–10.9	4.4	4.8	5.0	1.1
11.0–11.9	3.5	2.1	3.7	3.0
12.0–12.9	2.4	1.3	1.1	1.1
13.0–13.9	3.7	1.8	1.8	.8
14 and over	12.3	6.1	3.6	1.5

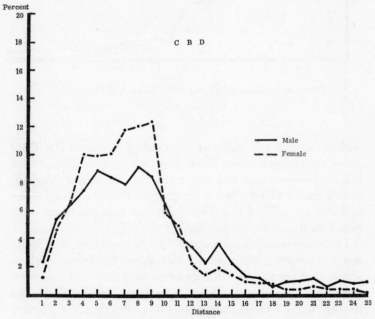

Distance Profiles—CBD Commuters: Male and Female

Figure II–2

II–2 and II–3, where percentage distributions by distance traveled are compared. In the West Suburban case, the major
difference is concentrated in the first two distance miles. The
median-mile figure for women is only 1.8 as compared with
4.1 for male suburban commuters. There are no such striking
contrasts in the CBD curves. It will be noted, however, that
the higher average distances for female commuters are decep-
tive. The percentage of all female commuters exceeds the percentage of all male commuters through much of the middle-
distance plateau zone, but beyond eleven miles there are more

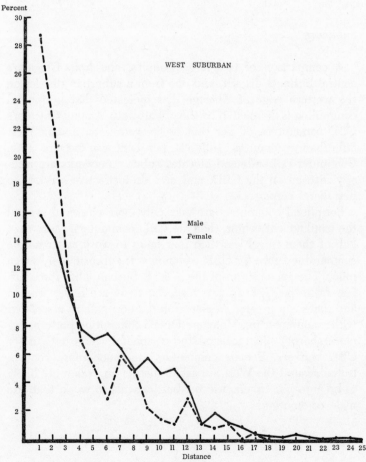

Distance Profiles—West Suburban Commuters: Male and Female

Figure II–3

male commuters, using either private auto or commuter railroads. The median-mile figure for men is actually somewhat
greater than for women. In general, this evidence taken with
the low figure for peripheral employment of women and for
female auto drivers, provides additional support to the statements in other studies as to the restricted work preference area
of the female worker. This area is more restricted among peripheral commuters than among CBD commuters because of
the absence of low-cost public transportation, which has ex-
tended the work preference area of the female CBD workers.

Summary

A comparison of two large samples, one from Chicago's
central business district, and one from a suburban district on
the western edge of Chicago, has indicated that peripheral
commuting is dominated by the private auto. Among Chicago's
CBD commuters, 30 per cent use private auto; among West
Suburban commuters, fully 84 per cent use private auto.
Commuter railroads and elevated-subway networks are radially focused on the CBD, and provide ineffective services to
peripheral centers.

Peripheral commuters are markedly more clustered around
the employment center, than are CBD commuters. More than
half of them travel less than four miles to work, whereas the
comparable figure for CBD commuters is approximately seven
miles. The composition of the West Suburban labor force differs from the CBD in two respects: there are fewer women
and there is a greater emphasis on the occupations associated
with manufacturing. Male and female commuting patterns are
more sharply differentiated for peripheral workers than for
CBD workers. Female commuters are much more concentrated around the West Suburban district and are more likely
to be auto passengers, use the bus, or walk to work, than are
male commuters.

CHAPTER III

Spatial Distribution of
Peripheral Commuters

Although certain aggregate distance relationships have been established, the spatial distribution of peripheral commuters has not yet been examined. In this chapter, therefore, the emphasis will be on a visual comparison of maps showing: (1) the spatial distribution of peripheral commuters and of commuters to other parts of the city; (2) a more detailed breakdown of the distribution of West Suburban commuters. Examination of these maps should provide a clearer view of the degree and nature of the concentration or dispersal of the peripheral laborshed, and a preliminary conception of its relation to population, distance, and other factors.

Data

The data on which the maps are based were collected by the Chicago Area Transportation Study in the spring and summer of 1956. They are largely based on 49,521 interviews conducted at every thirtieth dwelling place in the study area (the area bounded by the light dashed line in Figure III–1).[1] Mapping was done according to the grid cell pattern established by the study. As shown in Figure III–1, the area was put on a half-mile grid pattern. This resulted in over 5,000 grid cells,

[1] The authors would like to express their gratitude to J. Douglas Carroll, Jr., Director of the Chicago Area Transportation Study, Garred P. Jones, Supervisor of Graphics, and John J. Howe, Supervisor of Operations, for their cooperation in furnishing these data and answering questions pertaining to them. The sampling methods are discussed in Chicago Area Transportation Study, *Survey Findings,* Volume I (Chicago: Chicago Area Transportation Study, July, 1960), pp. 29–31.

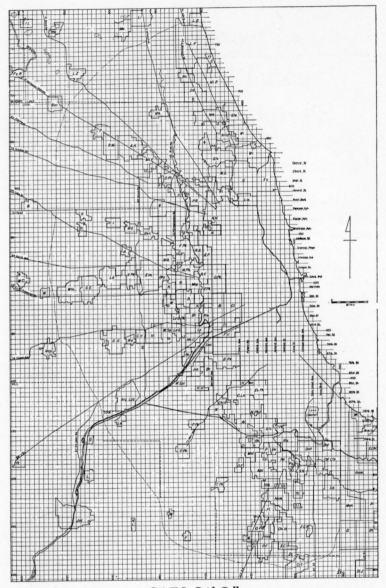

C.A.T.S. Grid Cells

Figure III-1

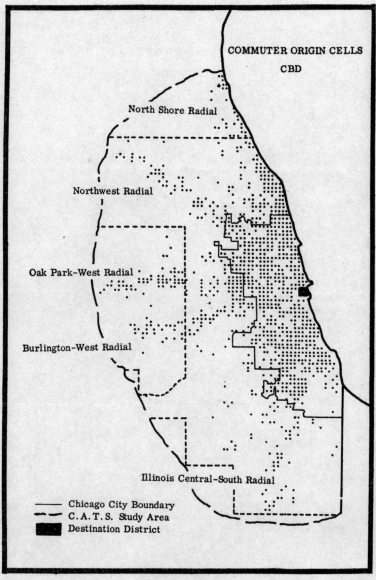

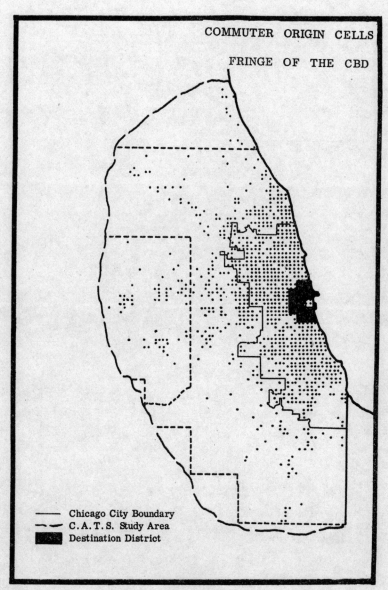

CBD Origin Cells

Figure III–3A

Origin Cells—Fringe of CBD

Figure III–3B

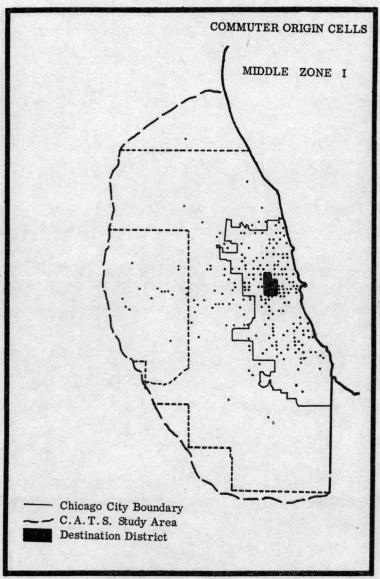

Origin Cells—Middle Zone I

Figure III–3C

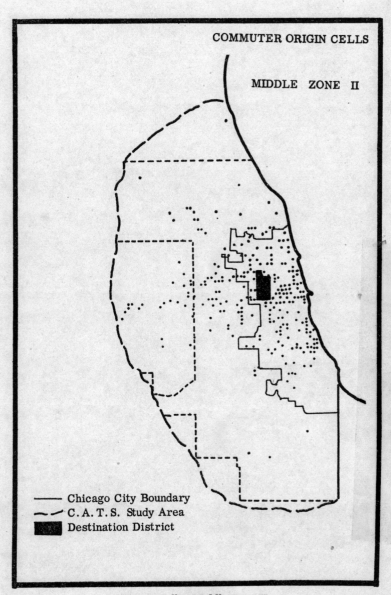

Origin Cells—Middle Zone II

Figure III–3D

each one-quarter square mile in area. The grid cells are located on a coordinate system, and all the home interviews are coded accordingly. For purposes of showing flow lines or travel desire lines (straight-line movement from origin cell to destination cells), a special machine called a cartographatron was developed.[2] Travel data is fed into the cartographatron on magnetic tape. As the tape is read, a light blip moves across the face of a cathode ray tube from the origin cell to the destination cell. Each trace is recorded on a photographic plate, thus giving a cumulative picture of traffic desire lines.

The origin-cell dot maps, Figures III–3A through III–4F (following p. 22) were drawn directly from cartographatron displays. As the tape was read, a light blip flashed on for each origin cell and was recorded on the negative, as is shown on Figure III–2 which shows the origin cells for all first work trips to the central business district. It should be noted that the resulting dot maps indicate only, that at least one CBD commuter originated in that cell. They do not indicate the number of commuters in each cell. Thus, the visual impression from the series of dot maps greatly overstates the degree of dispersion of the journey-to-work patterns, since one would expect the number of commuters from cells close to the destination district to be considerably greater than from the other cells. For comparative purposes, however, it is possible to note changes in the pattern of maximum dispersion as one examines laborsheds of: (a) different destination districts within the same sector from CBD to periphery; (b) different peripheral destination districts. Figure III–5 (see page 30) provides the basis for a more detailed examination of the commuter magnitudes, associated with each cell for one peripheral destination district. It is based on the actual number of commuters recorded in the one-in-thirty sample for each cell, as were the tables in Chapter II.

Sectoral Traverse

Figures III–3A through III–3F represent a traverse along one of Chicago's western sectors from the central business dis-

[2] The cartographatron is discussed in Chicago Area Transportation Study, Volume I, pp. 97–99.

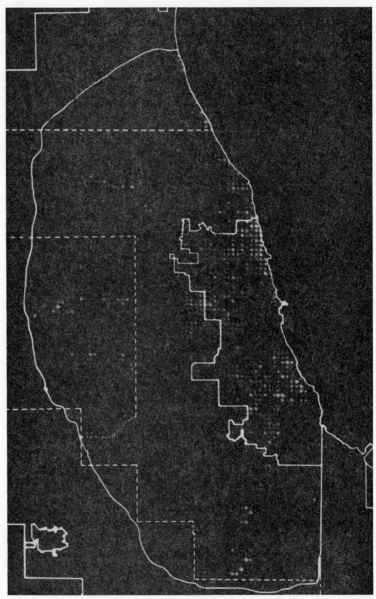

CBD Origin Cells—Cartographatron Display

Figure III–2

trict to the periphery of the city. In each case, the dots represent quarter-mile cells from which there has been at least one commuter to the specified destination district. The destination districts are Chicago Area Transportation Study Analysis Zones.[3] These have been arranged and numbered on a ring and sector basis. The traverse is taken along a western sector from the central business district out to Ring Five (the peripheral zone).

Figure III–3A shows the distribution of the commuter origin cells for work trips to the central business district. As would be expected, the dots cover most of Chicago's urbanized area. Within the city, there are CBD commuters from nearly all possible origin cells. Most of the blank spaces on the map represent non-residential areas. All of the radial suburbs are clearly delineated. Although the radials coincide with commuter rail lines, there are also many auto commuters from these areas. The concentration of dots is due, in part, to the effective rail and highway transport along these radials; in part, to the concentration of suburban population in these same zones—which, in turn, was originally associated with transportation advantages of the radials. Figure III–3B represents commuter travel to the next zone which corresponds roughly with the fringe of the central business district. The journey-to-work pattern is quite similar to the CBD pattern: dots cover most of the city and the radial suburbs are well defined, although not quite so clearly as in the case of the central business district. The sharpest change in commuting patterns occurs between Figure III–3B and Figure III–3C. The dots on Figure III–3C represent one-quarter square mile cells from which commuters travel to employment centers in a middle zone destination district at the fringe of the central business district. In this zone, the transportation advantages of the CBD have been lost. This is particularly true for outlying areas and sectors other than the western sector. There are very few origin cells in northern or southern suburban radials. The city itself is considerably less thoroughly covered with origin cells particularly north and south of the destination district. Although commuter origin cells are not tightly concentrated around the destination district in Figure III–3C, we can, how-

[3] Chicago Area Transportation Study, Volume I, p. 102.

ever, say that the pattern of maximum dispersal of the middle zone labor force is much less widely distributed over the city than is the pattern of maximum dispersal of the central business district. As one moves farther out into the middle zone (Figures III–3D and III–3E) essentially the same pattern prevails. The origin cells, although not strikingly concentrated, are by no means dispersed throughout the city and not all of the suburban radials are represented. In Figures III–3D and III–3E, three radials may be observed. In both cases, commuters converge from the Northwest Suburban radial, the Oak Park–West radial, and the Burlington-West radial. Very few cells within the interstitial suburban area originate commuters to middle zone destinations largely because of the low population densities. There is some difference between the middle zone maps in the degree to which non-adjacent parts of the city are represented. Note the differences between Figures III–3C and III–3E in this respect. Origin cells on the South Side are much less prominent on Figure III–3E than on Figure III–3C.

Figure III–3F represents the distribution of cells providing employees for the next destination district, which is in the suburban zone at the edge of the city. This is the West Suburban district from which the more detailed sample was taken. In general, the pattern is similar to the middle zone patterns which have preceded it: general dispersion with something of a concentration on adjacent areas. The chief difference is the importance of a single radial, the Oak Park–West radial, and the fact that there is a sprinkling of origin cells in the interstitial areas. The Northwest and Burlington–West radials are only weakly represented.

In summary, the sectoral traverse indicates an increased frictional effect of distance, as destination districts farther away from the center of the city are considered. This increased friction conforms with the distance comparisons in Chapter II and with the findings of other studies referred to earlier. In addition, the sequence indicates that the uneven distribution of population in the city must be considered together with the distance effect. There is a sprinkling of dots through much of the city in Figure III–3F despite distance from the West Suburban district because of the higher population density, which in itself increases the probability of a commuter to any em-

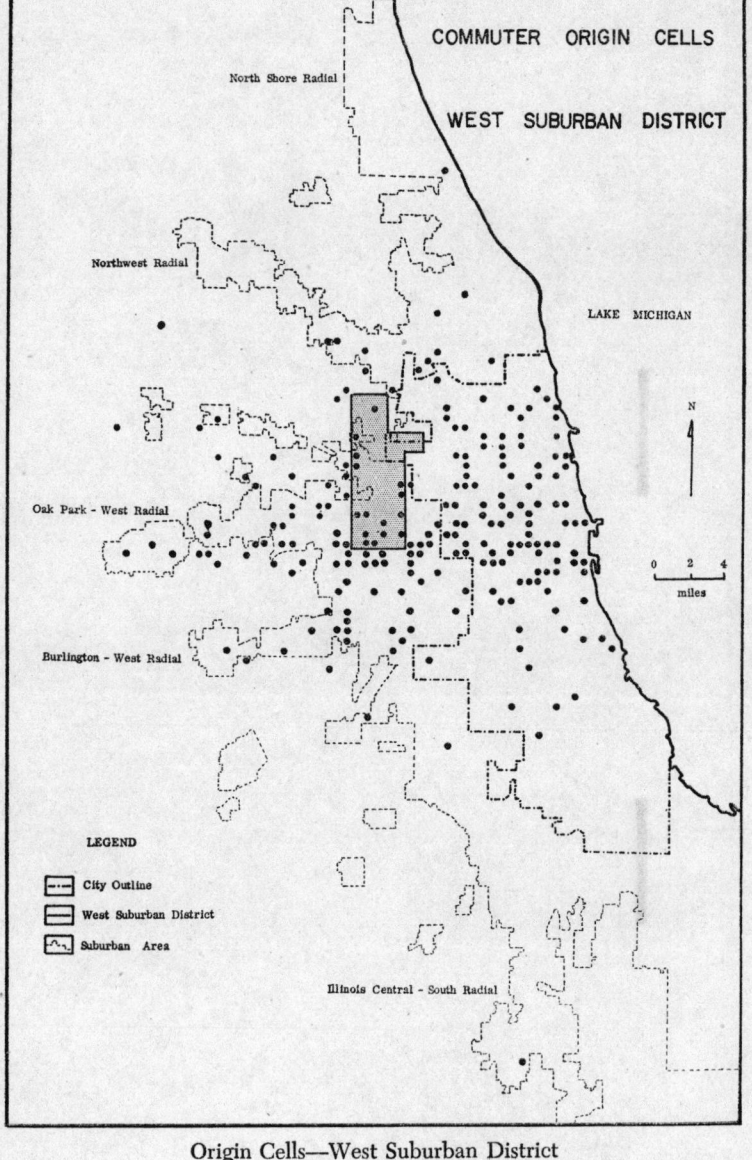

Origin Cells—West Suburban District

Figure III–4C

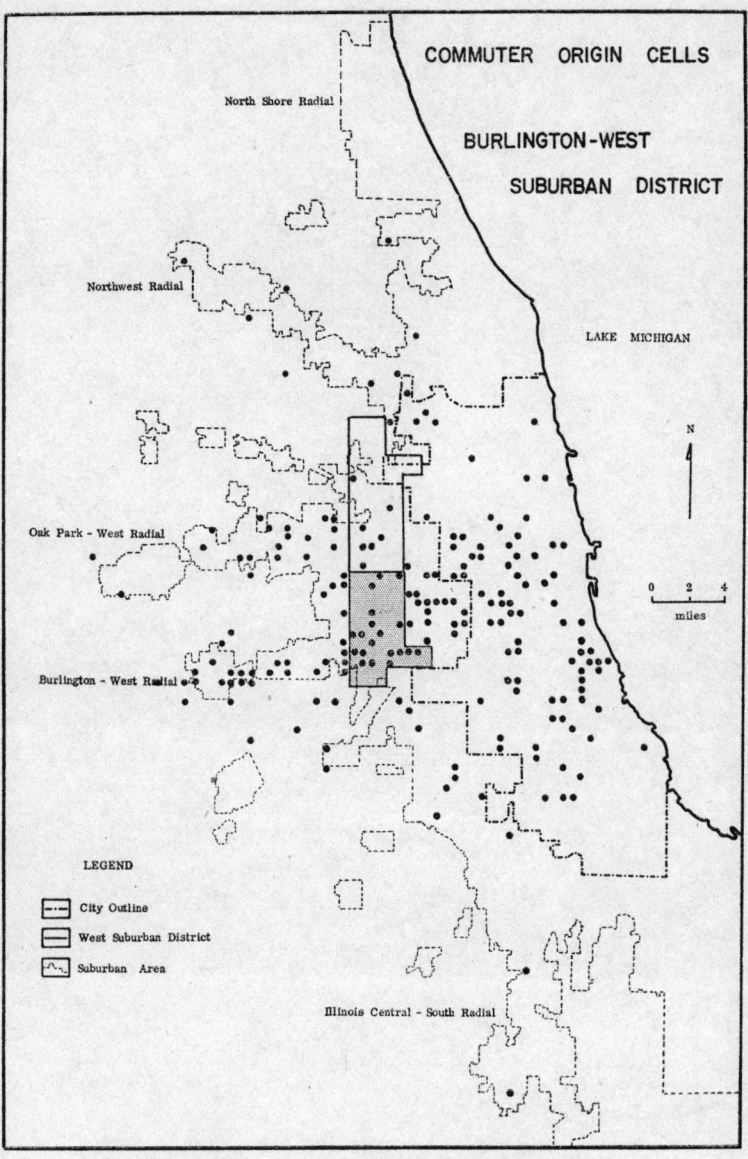

Origin Cells—Burlington-West Suburban District

Figure III–4D

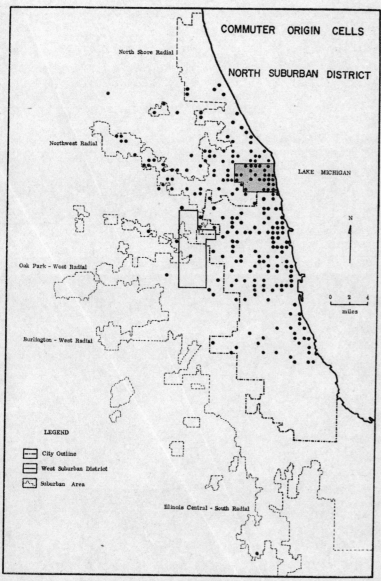

Origin Cells—North Suburban District
Figure III–4A

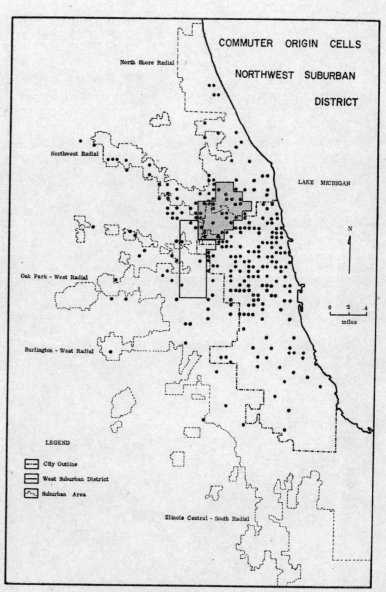

Origin Cells—Northwest Suburban District
Figure III–4B

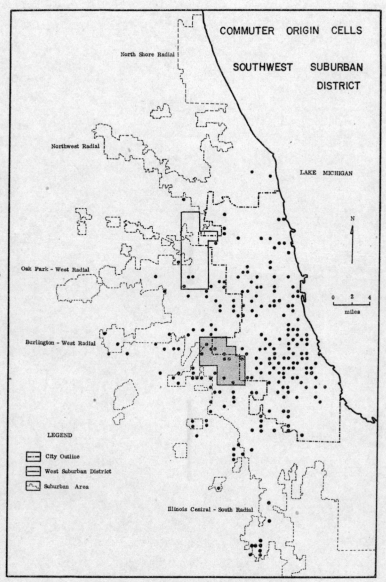

Origin Cells—Southwest Suburban District
Figure III–4E

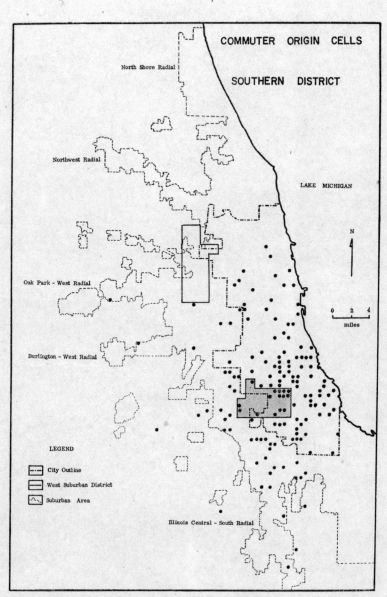

Origin Cells—Southern District
Figure III–4F

ployment center in the metropolitan area. This spill-over of the peripheral labor force into the city, particularly the adjacent portion of the city, was evident in the importance of reverse commuting noted in nearly all of the other studies.

Peripheral Traverse

Figures III–4A through III–4F show the journey-to-work patterns of each of the destination districts in the periphery (Ring Five), starting with the North Suburban district in the northern part of the city, and swinging in an arc around the periphery to the Southern district. These districts form an irregular band roughly between ten and fourteen miles from the central business district.

A survey of the six maps indicates a general similarity in the journey-to-work patterns of peripheral employment centers. The laborsheds are more restricted than those in the middle zone and the CBD, indicating the stronger frictional effect of distance. The effects of high population density in the city are evident in the origin-cell pattern. Another similarity may be noted between these six maps. There is a general emphasis on the adjacent suburban radial or pair of radials. This tendency was noted in the New York and Boston studies as well as by Reinemann, who also found a marked sectoral consistency in the outward migrations of industry itself.[4] Examination of the individual maps reveals several interesting variations on these basic themes. Figure III–4A the North Suburban district differs from the typical laborshed pattern in three respects: (1) the interstitial area is unusually well-represented; (2) the adjacent radial (North Shore) is by no means dominant; (3) there is a long extension of the laborshed inside the city to the South Side.

The prominence of the interstitial area is probably due to the higher population density, which has developed in parts of the interstitial suburban area, between the North Shore radial and the Northwest radial. There are many cells with estimated populations in excess of 1,000 persons in this zone, as compared to just a few such cells between all other suburban ra-

4 Reinemann, *op. cit.*, p. 164.

dials. In the future, rapidly growing auto-oriented suburban areas such as these should become increasingly important as source regions for peripheral workers. The second difference in the North Suburban map is probably associated with the unusually high-income nature of the North Shore radial. The New York study indicated the tendency for high-income executives and professional men to commute to the central business district from distant suburbs rather than to seek employment in the periphery.[5] This, coupled with the fact that the North Shore radial has better access to the central business district, than has any other sector, means that labor competition from the CBD is particularly acute along this radial for peripheral employment centers. The third difference is probably associated with a special characteristic of the labor force as well as with the low time-cost associated with the elevated lines which extend from the North Shore into Chicago's South Side. The low-income, densely populated Negro district provides a large number of domestic workers, who commute over the relatively inexpensive elevated system to meet the needs of North Shore suburbanites for domestic help.

The next three peripheral districts seem to conform fairly well to the general pattern (Figure III–4B, III–4C, and III–4D). The Burlington–West Suburban district's journey-to-work pattern, Figure III–4D, differs a bit in that two suburban radials are well represented. The two western radials are fairly close to each other, and the Burlington-West district's location between them makes it accessible to both. Figures III–4E and III–4F, the two southernmost destination districts in Ring Five, show a more marked change. The importance of suburban commuters is noticeably less than in the other four cases. The Illinois Central South radial does not contain as many commuter origin cells as one would expect from its population. In part, this is due to the fact that Chicago extends considerably farther south than it does west. As a result, parts of these two destination districts are located within the city. In part, also, it is due to the effects of competing employment centers. The Illinois Central Railroad operates high-speed, high-capacity commuter services focused on the central business district. The Calumet area, with its huge labor needs, is close enough to these districts to attract employees also.

[5] Hoover and Vernon, *op. cit.*, p. 160.

Thus, the peripheral traverse has provided further visual evidence of the importance of population density and distance. In addition, it has indicated the probable importance of adjacent suburban radials. There were also some suggestions on the maps of such factors as income, occupation, and alternate employment opportunities.

The West Suburban Commuter Pattern

Figures III–5 and III–6 provide a closer look at the distribution of commuters to the West Suburban district, which was compared to the CBD in Chapter II. This map differs from Figure III–4C in that it is based on the actual number of sampled commuters recorded for each cell. The one-quarter square mile cells have been grouped into square-mile cells for purposes of cartographic illustration. On Figure III–5 the area of each circle is proportional to the number of sampled West Suburban commuters in that square mile. The same numbers are used on Figure III–6, but isolines are used to separate the values.

On both maps, the concentrated nature of the pattern is evident. The largest circles and highest isoline categories cluster tightly around the West Suburban district, particularly in the southern portion, where the Oak Park–West radial intersects the peripheral zone. Thus, there is a greater frictional effect of distance than was apparent on the origin cell maps. The effects of population are evident in a number of medium-sized cells scattered through the city. The importance of the adjacent suburban radial is demonstrated by the stringing of medium-size circles along the Oak Park–West radial. For purposes of analysis, it will prove useful to treat the destination district as though all trips terminated at its center. This permits the establishment of broad distance zones around the district as shown in Figure III–7. The drop-off in commuter density (all circles represent commuters per square mile) with distance can be treated in a generalized fashion by listing the number of commuters in each band. Table III–1 represents a comparison of the figures obtained by this process of grouping commuters into distance bands, and the more accurate figures obtained by recording and grouping the actual distance

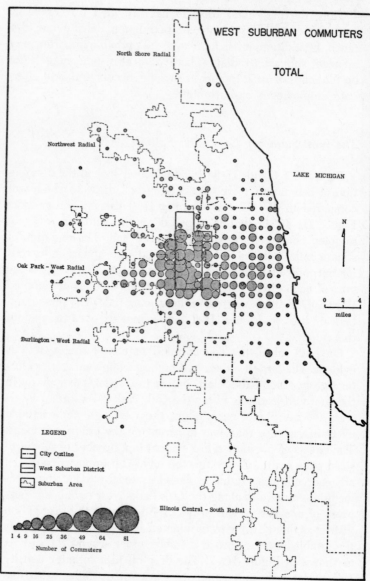

West Suburban Commuters—Graded Circles

Figure III–5

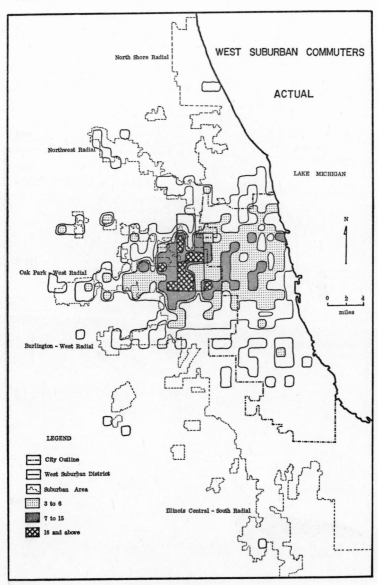

West Suburban Commuters—Isolines

Figure III–6

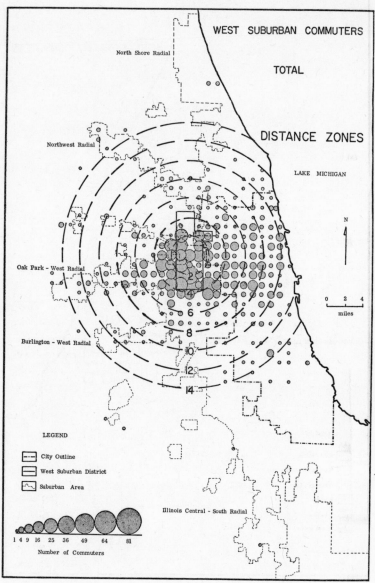

Distance Zones

Figure III–7

TABLE III–1

DISTANCE BANDS AND DISTANCE TRAVELED

Distance (miles)	Commuter Travel (per cent)	Commuters in Bands (per cent)
0– 4	53.53	48.9
4– 6	13.05	16.7
6– 8	11.05	14.3
8–10	8.88	9.3
10–12	7.66	5.2
12–14	2.70	2.3
14 and over	3.13	3.3

traveled by each commuter sampled (Table II–6, page 16). As would be expected, most of the discrepancy between the two columns is concentrated within the first two distance bands. The size of the West Suburban destination district is such that a commuter within the two- to four-mile band may actually have traveled shorter distances to places of employment near the margins of the district. Aggregation by distance bands results in a figure of 17 per cent in the zero to two-mile band, as opposed to 35 per cent for the actual distance traveled. In both cases, however, between 45 and 55 per cent of the peripheral commuters were in the zero to four-mile zone and the percentages correspond reasonably well outward from that zone. Thus, in most comparisons utilizing distance-band figures, the zero to four-mile band will be used as the innermost band, rather than the zero to two-mile band.

With the introduction of commuter magnitudes, it is possible to attempt a somewhat more accurate measurement of the nature and importance of simple distance and population effects on peripheral commuting. A multiple regression analysis was carried on with the number of commuters in a square-mile cell treated as though it were a linear function of the population in that cell, and distance from the center of the cell to the center of the destination district.[6] The results indicate that only 17 per cent of the variation in commuters per square mile is statistically explained by population and distance in an unmodified form.

[6] In all cases, number of commuters refers to the number of commuters in the C.A.T.S. sample.

The estimating equation is:

$$(C_{ij}) = 9.24 + 0.00004\ (P_i) - 0.6\ (D_{ij})$$

Where: C_{ij} = The number of commuters between the origin cell i and the destination district j

  P_i = Population of origin cell i

  D_{ij} = Straight-line distance between origin cell i and center of destination district j

When all three variables are transformed to logarithms, so as to normalize them and provide a closer fit to the probably curvilinear form of the functional relationship, 46 per cent of the variation in logarithms of commuter totals is statistically explained. In this form the estimating equation is:

$$(\log C_{ij}) = 0.51 + 0.2\ (\log P_i) - 1.06\ (\log D_{ij})$$

$$\text{or: } C_{ij} = 3.2\ \frac{(P_i)^{0.2}}{(D_{ij})^{1.06}}$$

This is essentially a gravity-model type of formulation and indicates that in this case the best exponent of distance is approximately one. Thus when population is accounted for, the average effect of distance on the generation of peripheral commuters is best represented by distance raised to the first power. This figure is higher than figures which have been obtained for intraurban travel in some other studies; lower than figures which have been obtained for travel between cities.[7]

Summary

An examination of a number of maps comparing commuting patterns in different parts of the city has indicated that the peripheral pattern is more tightly clustered around the destination district. The basic forces affecting the probability of a worker commuting between a given residential cell and the West Suburban district are the population of the residential cell and its distance from the district. This is not a simple linear relationship and deserves more investigation. Adjacent

[7] For a general discussion of the gravity model see Gerald A. P. Carrothers, *Journal of the American Institute of Planners* (Spring, 1956), pp. 94–102. For some examples of the application of the gravity model to urban transportation see the special issue of the *Journal of the American Institute of Planners*, Vol. XXV No. 2 (May, 1959).

suburban radials generate many peripheral commuters although it is not clear yet whether or not they generate more than their population and distance would lead one to expect. It also seemed from the maps that income, occupational structure, and the presence of alternate employment opportunities affect the spatial distribution of the peripheral labor force.

CHAPTER IV

The Application of Probability Models to the Peripheral Commuter Pattern

One approach to the further investigation of the spatial distribution of peripheral commuters is the use of a probability model, based on stated postulates, to simulate successive commuter distributions and compare them with the actual distribution. The models used could be considered as static versions of the Monte Carlo simulation of diffusion, used by Torsten Hägerstrand.[1]

The reason for using this type of model, is the feeling that the West Suburban sample of commuter trips contains a strong random element. Underlying the aggregated commuting pattern shown on Figure III–5, page 30, are countless decisions made by individuals as to their place of employment. For some of these, a rationale may be inferred from the commuting maps. Distance, for instance, seems to bear some sort of non-

---

[1] Torsten Hägerstrand, "On the Monte Carlo Simulation of Diffusion," *Quantitative Geography*, ed. William L. Garrison (New York: Atherton Press, forthcoming). Hägerstrand's model simulated the process whereby an innovation or idea spreads out from a center. His model was dynamic, in that it was run for several time periods. The probabilities for each successive time period were affected by the events of the preceding period. For other examples of the use of simulation in geographic study see John D. Nystuen, "A Theory and Simulation of Intraurban Travel," *ibid.*; and Torsten Hägerstrand, "Migration and Area: Survey of a Sample of Swedish Migration Fields and Hypothetical Considerations on Their Genesis," *Migration in Sweden*, ed. Hannerberg, Hägerstrand and Odeving, Lund Studies in Geography, Series B., No. 13 (Lund: 1957), pp. 132–155.

random relation to place of employment decisions. Many individual decisions are such, however, that no overall rationale is apparent from the aggregated pattern. These decisions are assumed to be randomly distributed, since there is no reason to believe that they are more likely to occur in one part of the metropolitan area than another. One of the problems in analyzing the commuter pattern, therefore, is to distinguish between those aspects of the pattern for which a rationale may be inferred, i.e., those following non-random processes, and those which seem merely to be the result of random processes.

The first step in a Monte Carlo model is to establish certain decision rules to represent those processes for which a rationale has been inferred. Specific probabilities are then assigned to each cell based only on these rules of the game. The random processes can be represented by throwing dice, drawing numbers from a hat, or drawing from a table of random numbers. Each of these randomly obtained numbers allocates a commuter to a particular cell. In the West Suburban case, for instance, the procedure was to: (1) assign to every cell in the city a probability of originating a commuter to the West Suburban district based on certain specified assumptions such as population and distance relationships; (2) cumulate these probabilities so that they add up to 1.0, and so that each cell in the resulting probability surface has a specified range of numbers, such as .0635 to .0639; (3) look up a random number for each commuter to be distributed and assign him to the indicated cell. The four-digit random number 0637, for instance, would be assigned to the cell cited above. Thus, if 1,000 random numbers were used to assign simulated commuters to cells according to probabilities based on the assumed non-random processes, the result would be a map in which there was both a systematic element and an element based on random choice. Each simulation map would represent one sample of how a commuting pattern could look if the only non-random process at work were the postulated population-distance relationship. Any clusters or alignments on the map would be regarded either as a result, solely of these population-distance relationships, or as a purely random occurrence. If a series of simulation maps based on the same postulates were to show the same clusters, then it would be assumed that the clusters were inherent in the population-distance relationships.

If they did not persistently recur, their presence on the first map would be presumed to be a random occurrence.

In this chapter, simulated maps will be compared with the actual map. A persistent discrepancy between simulated and actual commuter patterns would suggest the existence of a non-random process, not included in the model. For example, a clustering of commuters in a particular sector of the metropolitan area may show up on the actual map but not on the simulated maps. This would indicate that some factor in that sector tends to generate more commuters than would be expected from the population-distance relationships built into the model. New decision rules would therefore be formulated, incorporating additional probabilities for the newly observed non-random processes. By such progressive modifications of a set of probabilities based on simple population and distance relations, a set of statements will be developed which provide a condensed description of the spatial distribution of peripheral commuters.

Model I—Population and Distance

The importance of population and distance were established in the preceding chapter. In setting up the decision rules for a first simulated map of West Suburban commuters, therefore, it seems reasonable to base them on these two factors. Model I was constructed on the two following assumptions: (1) the probability of a West Suburban commuter originating from a given cell is directly proportional to the population of that cell; (2) the probability of a West Suburban commuter originating from a given cell is inversely proportional to the distance between the cell and the center of the West Suburban district. Following the results of the regression analysis, the average exponent of distance is considered to be one. This means that the population of every cell was divided by the distance from the center of the West Suburban district in order to give an estimate of the probability of generating a West Suburban commuter. These numbers were cumulated for the entire city and each cell was then expressed as a percentage of the total. A commuting pattern was then simulated by selecting 250 random numbers and assigning them to an appropriate cell on the probability surface. Figure IV–1A presents the resulting isoline map. Table IV–1 presents the comparison of the results of this simulation with the actual distribution of commuters by distance bands from the center of the West Suburban district. The striking contrast between the simulation map (Figure IV–1A) and the actual map (Figure IV–1B) is the result of the clear understatement of the friction of distance in the simple P/D model.[2] Commuters are much more widely distributed through the city in the simulated pattern than in the actual pattern. Whereas nearly one-half of the actual commuters

TABLE IV–1

SIMULATED AND ACTUAL COMMUTERS–MODEL I

Distance Band (miles)	Actual (per cent)	Model I (per cent)
0– 4	48.9	19
4– 6	16.7	15
6– 8	14.3	17
8–10	9.3	16
10–12	5.2	11
12–14	2.3	8
14 and over	3.3	14

originate inside of the four-mile band, only 19 per cent of the simulated commuters fall within this band. Only 11 per cent of the actual commuters originate from beyond the ten-mile band as compared to 33 per cent of the simulated commuters. Thus, the first modification of the model is to alter the distance assumption. A higher overall exponent would not seem justified, in view of the fact that an exponent of one has provided

[2] It became clear after a few initial experiments that, in most instances, the large number of observations involved in this study rendered repeated simulations unnecessary. Consistent discrepancies became evident early in the process, and the replications which were attempted in early formulations did not add new information. Thus, only one simulation is used for comparative purposes in this study, although repeated simulations are more in keeping with the logic of the model. In most cases this does not affect the validity of the conclusions. In some instances, however, where the results are analyzed in detail, a single simulation does not provide conclusive evidence of nonrandomness of a particular discrepancy between actual and observed results, despite the large total number of observations.

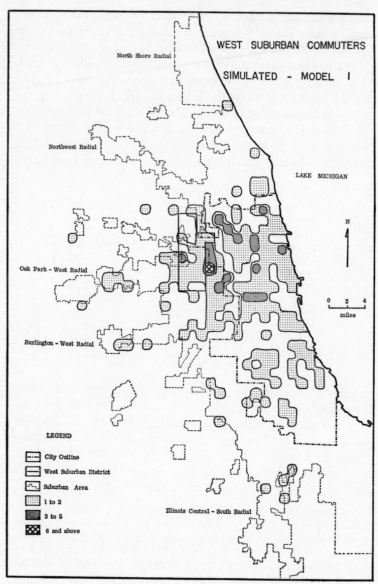

Simulated West Suburban Commuters—Model I
Figure IV–1A

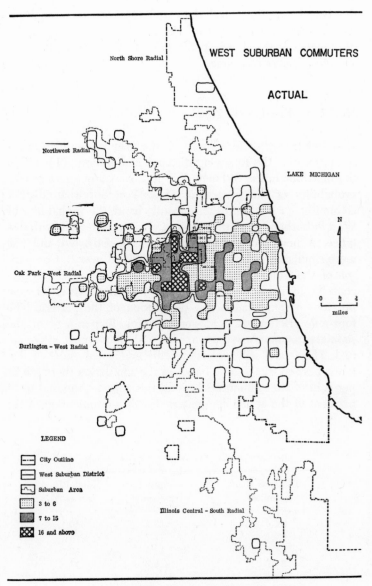

Actual West Suburban Commuters
Figure IV–1B

the best fit to the travel data and the regression analysis. Examination of the map and the consideration of the great discrepancy within the first four miles lead to the postulate of an inner frictionless zone.

Model II—Frictionless Zone

Model II is therefore based on the original population assumption plus the following distance assumption: (1) within the first four miles, distance does not exert any effect on the probability of the generation of a West Suburban district commuter; (2) beyond the four-mile band, the probability of West Suburban commuter generation varies inversely with distance. A new probability surface was constructed and 250 more simulated commuters were distributed over it. Comparison of the isoline maps, Figures IV–2A and B, and the percentages in Table IV–2 suggests that the distance effect now provides a somewhat better description of the pattern. The four-mile frictionless zone accounts for 40 per cent of the simulated commuters, as compared with 50 per cent in the actual. The model still understates the additional effect of distance beyond the 10-mile band. In the simulation there are 24 per cent of the commuters beyond this zone as opposed to 11 per cent of the actual commuters. Further examination of the

TABLE IV–2

SIMULATED AND ACTUAL COMMUTERS—MODEL II

Distance Band (miles)	Actual (per cent)	Model II (per cent)
0– 4	48.9	40
4– 6	16.7	13
6– 8	14.3	12
8–10	9.3	11
10–12	5.2	9
12–14	2.3	4
14 and over	3.3	11
Adjacent Suburban Radial	58	30

two maps indicates that the model fails to take account of another aspect of the peripheral commuting pattern noted in the visual comparison of the map sequences in Chapter II—the emphasis on the adjacent suburban radial. The simulation map shows much less concentration on the adjacent radial than the map of actual commuters. Only 30 per cent of the simulated commuters originated from the adjacent radial as compared to 58 per cent of the actual.

Model III—Adjacent Suburban Radial

A new postulate was therefore added to the model. It was assumed that the probability of a West Suburban commuter originating from a cell in an adjacent radial was twice that of an origination from a cell which was not in an adjacent suburban radial. The problem of defining the adjacent suburban radial was eased by drawing upon the study by Pierre de Vise, *A Social Geography of Chicago*, published by the Northeastern Metropolitan Area Planning Commission.[3] On the basis of socio-economic data, transportation, density, and other criteria, de Vise divided the suburban area of Chicago into twelve sectors. Only two of these sectors might be considered as adjacent to the West Suburban district. Model III was, therefore, used in the construction of a new probability surface based on a doubled probability of commuter origination for any cell within those two sectors, as well as on the population and distance assumptions of Model II. Figures IV–3A and B, the isoline maps, and Table IV–3, the summary of the distribution of 250 simulated commuters, provide a better description of the actual commuter pattern than was true of the two preceding models. On both simulated and actual distributions, there is a marked clustering inside the four-mile frictionless zone and a concentration on the adjacent suburban radial. Closer examination, however, reveals three discrepancies between the two distributions which might be regarded as nonrandom: (1) the model's continued overstatement of commuters beyond approximately 10 miles; (2) the model's

[3] Northeastern Illinois Metropolitan Area Planning Commission, *A Social Geography of Metropolitan Chicago* (Chicago: Northeastern Illinois Metropolitan Area Planning Commission, June, 1960), Map 7.

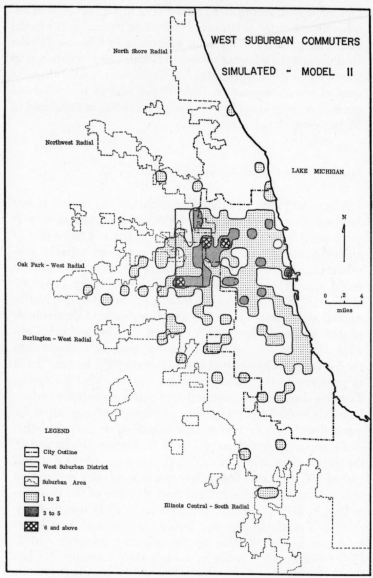

Simulated West Suburban Commuters—Model II
Figure IV–2A

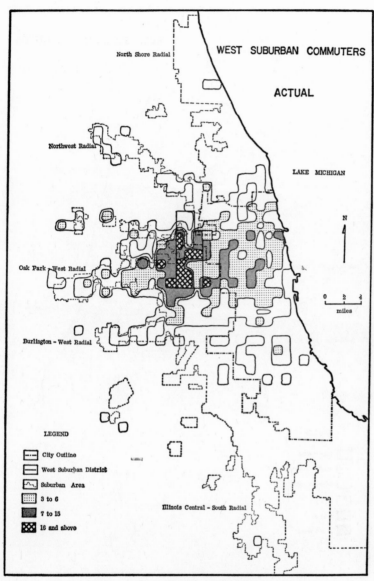

Actual West Suburban Commuters
Figure IV–2B

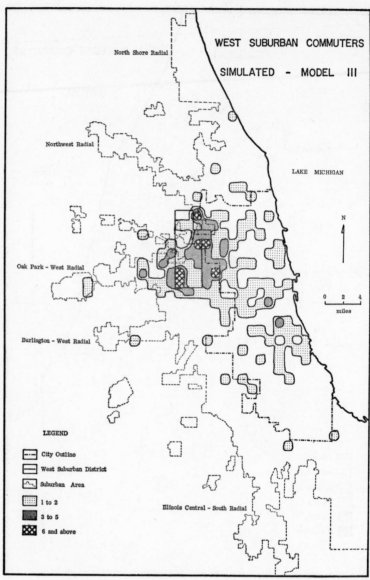

Simulated West Suburban Commuters—Model III
Figure IV–3A

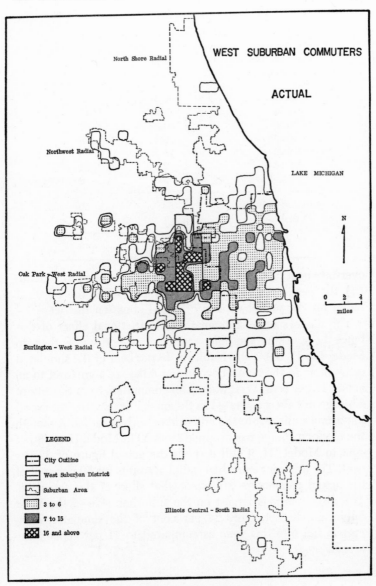

Actual West Suburban Commuters

Figure IV–3B

TABLE IV-3

SIMULATED AND ACTUAL COMMUTERS—MODEL III

Distance Bands (miles)	Actual (per cent)	Model III (per cent)
0– 4	48.9	55
4– 6	16.7	12
6– 8	14.3	7
8–10	9.3	8
10–12	5.2	6
12–14	2.3	4
14 and over	3.3	8
Adjacent Suburban Radial	58	50
City	32.2	43

overstatement of the importance of city commuters in general; (3) the persistence of some understatement of the adjacent radial on the suburban side of the destination district.

The model's understatement of the frictional effect of distance beyond the ten-mile zone is less noticeable than in Model I or II, but it still results in 18 per cent of the simulated commuters in the zones beyond ten miles, as compared to an actual 11 per cent. West Suburban commuters from the city of Chicago are also overstated in the model despite the increased importance allotted to the adjacent suburban radial. Although the city percentage has dropped from 59 in Model II to 43 per cent in Model III, it still exceeds the actual figure of 32 per cent. The adjacent suburban radial accounts for 50 per cent of the actual commuters, still somewhat short of the actual 58. The discrepancy is largest on the suburban side of the West Suburban district. Only 24 per cent of the simulated commuters fall into this zone as compared to 41 per cent of the actual.

Model IV

At this point several different experiments were attempted to control the interrelated effects noted in the discrepancy between Model III and the actual pattern. In one experiment, the distance exponent was increased to two beyond ten miles. This resulted in a badly overstated frictional effect with only two per cent of all simulated commuters originating from beyond the ten-mile band. These experiments led to Model IV in which the distance beyond ten miles is not raised to a power but is assumed to have twice the deterrent effect on commuting as is true of distance in the four- to ten-mile zone. To compensate for the overstatement of city commuters, suburban cells are given twice the probability of city cells of originating a West Suburban commuter; to compensate for the understatement for the suburban side of the adjacent radial, the doubling of probability is confined to that side. Thus, Model IV was based on the following postulates:

1. The probability of a cell generating a West Suburban commuter is directly proportional to the population of that cell.

2. The relation between distance and the probability of commuter origination is not a continuous one, but differs in the following fashion as one moves away from the destination district:

(a) distance is assumed to exert no deterrent effect within an inner frictionless zone, four miles in radius; (b) between four and ten miles, from the destination district the probability of commuter origination is inversely proportional to distance; (c) beyond ten miles, distance exerts a strongly deterrent effect, and probability is inversely proportional to twice the distance.

3. Cells located in adjacent suburban radials on the suburban side of the destination district have twice as great a probability of originating West Suburban commuters as do other cells with the same population and distance from the West Suburban district. Cells on the city-side of the adjacent radial are treated the same as city cells in this model.

4. Cells located outside the city of Chicago have twice as great a probability of originating West Suburban commuters as do cells inside the city, considering their population, distance, and location in a suburban radial.

Figure IV-4 shows the resulting probabilities expressed in population and distance terms for different parts of the city. When 250 commuters were distributed according to these probabilities, there seemed to be a fair correspondence in

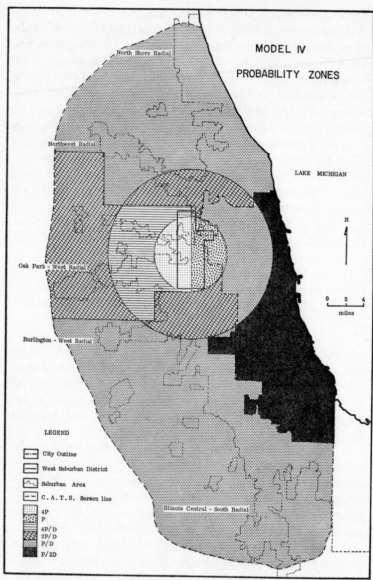

Probability Zones—Model IV

Figure IV-4

broad general outline as is shown in Figures IV–5A and B. The simulation was, therefore, continued until some 1150 commuters had been distributed, the same number that appeared in the West Suburban sample. Table IV–4 indicates a fairly

TABLE IV–4

SIMULATED AND ACTUAL COMMUTERS—MODEL IV

Distance Bands (miles)	Actual (per cent)	Model IV (per cent)
0– 4	48.9	53.4
4– 6	16.7	15.2
6–8	14.3	13.1
8–10	9.3	8.8
10–12	5.2	3.7
12–14	2.3	2.2
14 and over	3.3	3.6
Adjacent Suburban Radial	58	53
City	32.2	33.6

high degree of correspondence between simulated and actual distribution. The distance-band figures are quite close. The simulated commuters are shown on Figure IV–6 and the actual commuters on Figure IV–7. The similarity between the two maps is clear. There are now 34 per cent of simulated commuters originating in the city of Chicago, as compared to 32 per cent of the actual; there are 53 per cent of the simulated commuters in the adjacent radial, as compared to 58 per cent of the actual. There are, of course, many points of difference between the two maps, some related to the randomness involved in the simulation; some related to non-random processes other than those assumed in Model IV.

As a further check on the general descriptive efficiency of Model IV, the commuter values on both maps were aggregated to two-mile square grid cells and a regression was run between simulated and actual commuters for each two-mile square cell. The resulting correlation coefficient of .92 indicates that some 84 per cent of the variation in the actual commuter distribution can be statistically explained by relating it to variations in the distribution of artificial commuters assigned to

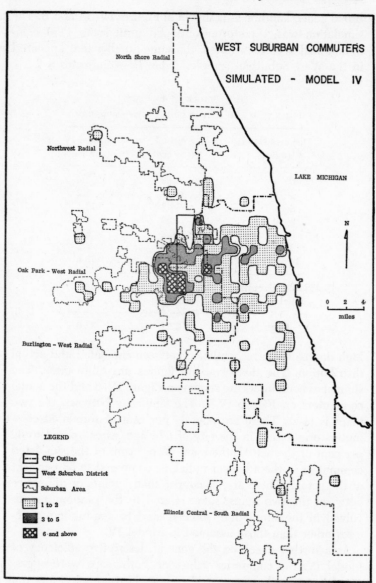

Simulated West Suburban Commuters—Model IV—Isolines
Figure IV–5A

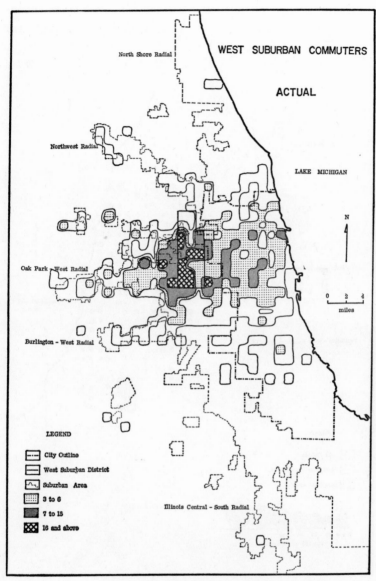

Actual West Suburban Commuters
Figure IV–5B

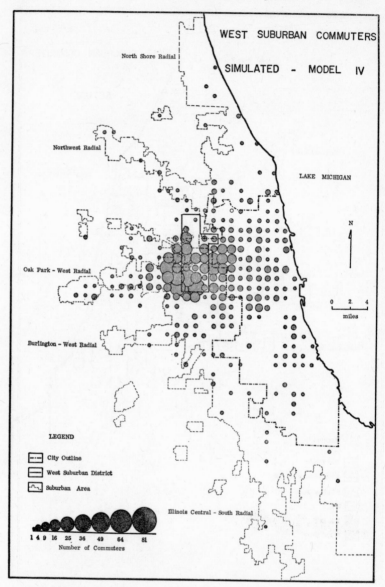

Simulated West Suburban Commuters—Model IV—Graded Circles
Figure IV–6

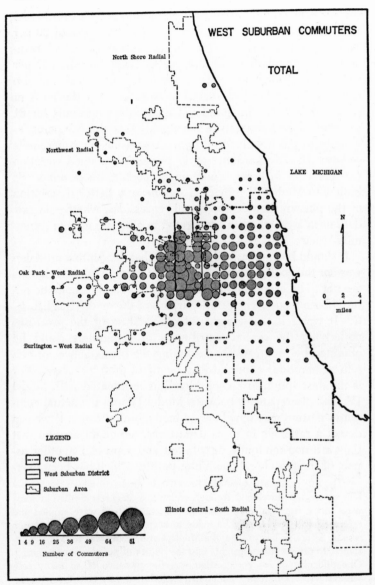

West Suburban Commuters—Graded Circles
Figure IV–7

various cells on the basis of the assumptions built into Model IV. This figure compares favorably with the figure of 26 per cent explained variation for the regression of actual commuters on population and distance by two-mile cells (67 per cent when all data were expressed in logs).[4] A test was also run at a lower level of spatial aggregation. On the basis of square mile cells, the simulated distribution accounts for 61 per cent of the variations in the actual. This also compares favorably to the population-distance regression for square-mile cells which shows a figure of 17 per cent explained variation (46 per cent in logs). Thus, on all counts, the assumptions built into Model IV provide a significantly better description of the pattern than do the initial regressions, whether in raw data or in logs, whether aggregated to a square mile or a two-mile square basis.

It should be emphasized, however, that descriptive precision was not the goal of this procedure. Extremely high correlations are not to be expected, in view of the inherently stochastic nature of the model. The prime purpose of the model was heuristic. It was felt that insight into the nature of the processes underlying the spatial distribution of commuters could be obtained by progressively examining the consequences of certain assumptions about, at least, some of these processes. Nor is the description to be considered as terminated with Model IV. The discrepancies between Model IV and the actual commuter pattern may now be examined more critically. If we can detect a rationale in these departures, we might assume that they are non-randomly distributed and represent another aspect of the peripheral commuter pattern which has been over-

[4] The use of a static type of Monte Carlo model in which the probabilities are not developed through successive stages is similar in some ways to the use of a regression. For this reason, both were applied and reference will occasionally be made to regression as well as simulation results. Although less precise, the Monte Carlo model was felt, in this instance, to provide more insights into the nature of peripheral commuting. One difficulty in using regression was the presence of so many cells without West Suburban commuters. Excluding empty cells from the regression affects the measurement of the distance effect, since the number of empty cells increases as one moves farther from the center. Other difficulties included: the necessity for using a complex distance function; the interpretation of data which have been transformed so as to normalize them and stabilize the variance; the large number of sporadically occurring dichotomous variables.

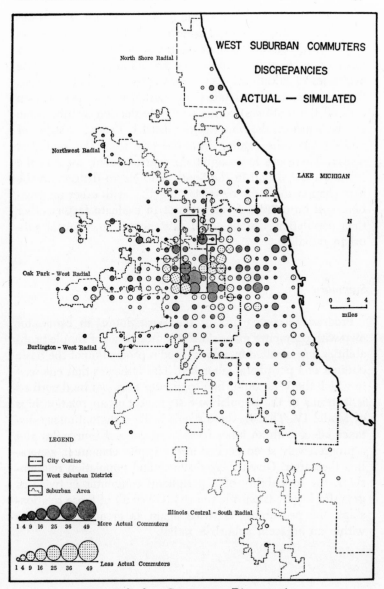

West Suburban Commuters—Discrepancies

Figure IV–8

looked in the assumptions of Model IV. These differences between actual and simulated patterns are shown separately on Figure IV–8, the discrepancy map. Cursory examination indicates a number of clusterings of highs and lows, which may be evidences of additional non-random processes. For example, the model tends to overstate the importance of some suburban cells off the southwest corner of the destination district, some city cells just off the center of the district. There is a string of understated cells leading into the city from the southeast corner. There are low-magnitude overstatement areas in the Northern radial and in the South Side Negro district. In the next chapter these discrepancies, together with other information, will be utilized in an attempt to evaluate factors other than population, distance, and existence of an adjacent suburban radial.

Summary

Progressive comparison of the West Suburban commuter map with commuter maps simulated from a set of simple probabilities, has resulted in a fairly good reproduction of the basic outlines of a peripheral laborshed. This indicates that one way in which the West Suburban commuter map can be described is in terms of the population-distance-suburban relationships of Model IV. That is, there seems to be a discontinuous distance effect with an inner frictionless zone of four miles and a progressively steep decline in per capita commuter generation thereafter. Given these distance and population relationships, the probability of a peripheral commuter is twice as great for locations outside the city. Given all of these relationships, the probability is twice again as great for locations within an adjacent suburban radial.

CHAPTER V

Other Factors Affecting the Peripheral Commuter Pattern

The Monte Carlo model developed in chapter four describes the total peripheral commuter pattern in terms of a set of generalized population, distance, and suburban location relationships. This aggregated pattern and these broad relationships may now be examined more critically in hopes of obtaining further insights into the nature of the interrelations between certain additional factors and the postulates of Model IV. Three additional factors will be examined in this chapter: (1) composition of the labor force; (2) the spatial distribution of income; (3) the spatial distribution of alternate employment opportunities.

Composition of the Labor Force

Many writers have noted the effects of labor force composition on the journey-to-work. Hoover and Vernon have reported on the different commuting patterns associated with sex, race, and occupation;[1] Burtt has noted the existence of localized supplies of labor clearly defined by occupation and sex.[2]

SEX

When the total peripheral labor force is divided according to sex, there is a noticeable contrast in the two resulting laborsheds, as is shown in Figure V–1 and V–2. Although both patterns show a clustering around the southern end of the destina-

---

[1] Hoover and Vernon, *op. cit.*, pp. 154–162.

[2] Burtt, *Changing Labor Supply Characteristics Along Route 128*, p. 29.

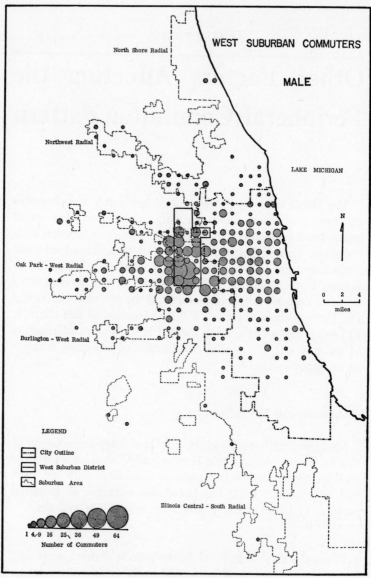

West Suburban Commuters—Male

Figure V–1

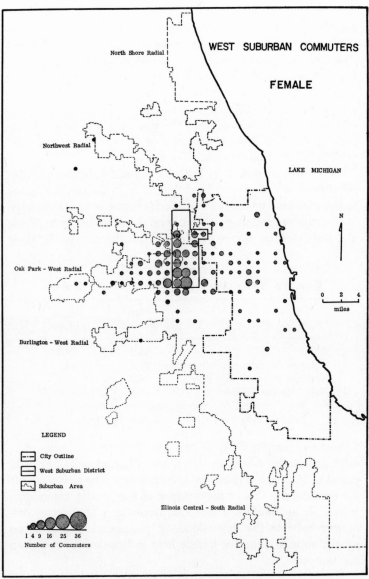

West Suburban Commuters—Female

Figure V–2

tion district, the female commuters are considerably more tightly clustered than are the male commuters. As noted in the CBD comparisons, this tighter clustering results in a 1.8 median-mile commuting distance for women, as compared to 4.1 for men, which indicates that more than one-half of the females commute less than two miles to work in peripheral employment centers. As was noted earlier, this restricted work preference area is associated with the generally low wages of female workers and the dominance of the private auto in the peripheral journey-to-work.

A comparison of Figures V–1 and V–2 also indicates a higher proportion of male reverse commuters from the city and other radial suburbs, whereas female commuters are concentrated in the adjacent radial, particularly on the suburban side. Table V–1 indicates the degree to which this is the case in the West

TABLE V–1

MALE AND FEMALE COMMUTERS—WEST SUBURBAN DISTRICT

	Male (per cent)	Female (per cent)
City	34.2	23.3
Adjacent Suburb*a*—Suburban Side	35.2	57.4
Adjacent Suburb—City Side	19.0	14.7
Non-Adjacent Suburb	11.6	4.6

a Adjacent suburb refers to adjacent suburban radial.

Suburban example. Fully 57 per cent of the female commuters originate on the suburban side of the adjacent radial, as compared to 35 per cent of the male commuters. The city accounts for considerably lower percentages of the female commuters than male commuters. These low percentages of reverse commuters indicate the dependence of peripheral employers on nearby supply areas, for female help in low-density suburban communities.

The first step in disaggregating the West Suburban commuter pattern, therefore, indicates that a different set of probabilities would have to be applied, if the commuter pattern were to be disaggregated by sex. In order to describe the female commuter pattern the basic model would probably need no change, but some of the weights and dimensions would be modified. The most likely modification would be to postulate a more restricted frictionless zone, and an increased positive effect attached to location within the adjacent suburban sector.

RACE

Figure V–3 is an extreme example of nonconformity to the general peripheral pattern. Residential segregation renders non-white peripheral commuters an obviously separate component of the aggregate pattern. Distance relationships take on a different meaning when viewed in a context of limited residential choice. The fact that most of the non-white population of Chicago is relatively far away from the West Suburban district is, of course, associated with the low figures for non-white commuters. Only 69 of the 1150 commuters in the sample were classed as non-white as compared to 14 per cent of the CBD commuters. Industries requiring large supplies of this generally low-wage labor have evidently not located in this peripheral destination district.

The non-white commuters form a strongly localized pattern on Figure V–3 at three well-defined source regions. The closest of these is in a portion of the suburb of Maywood, within the destination district itself, one of the relatively few areas of Negro population in the Chicago Suburban area. The largest group of non-white peripheral commuters is in the Negro district of Chicago's West Side. Most of these commuters are located along such thoroughfares as Madison Street, which provide better mass transit connections, at least to the southern margins of the destination district, than do other city areas, at a comparable distance. The third cluster is on Chicago's South Side. Despite its huge labor pool this area accounts for only a few West Suburban commuters. Well developed el-subway connections to the CBD make the arduous trip to the West Suburban district an even less attractive alternative than its distance would warrant. It is interesting to compare Chicago's weakly developed non-white reverse commuter flow with the statements made by Hoover and Vernon.[3] They found not only a strong reverse flow of non-white commuters, but also some fairly well developed non-white communities within the

[3] Hoover and Vernon, *op. cit.*, p. 213.

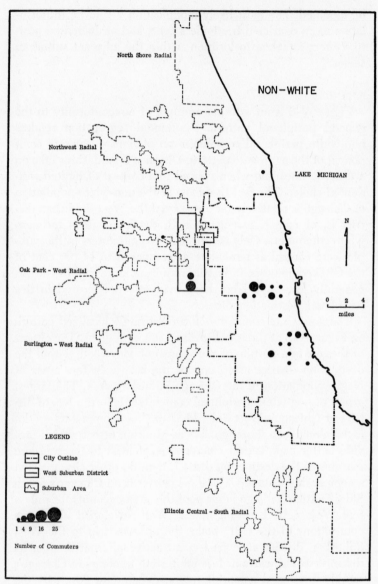

West Suburban Commuters—Non-White
Figure V–3

old cities at the inner ring of suburbs. In the West Suburban case, however, a logical modification in the probability model for non-white areas would seem to be a slight decrease in probability.

OCCUPATIONS

Figures V–4 through V–21 present the results of disaggregating the total commuter flow by broad occupational types. The maps are diverse enough to warrant separate consideration of commuting patterns associated with different occupational types, although the contrasts are not as great as for the sex and race distinctions. Some caution should be exercised in the visual interpretation of these maps. In comparison to the larger maps they all tend to overstate the apparent dispersion of the subgroup commuters. In part, this is due to the visually disproportionate weight given to single-commuter cells, which form a larger part of the total, as the number of commuters decreases. The principal utility of the map sequence, therefore, is for purposes of comparison between the occupational types themselves. Tabular material and distance profiles are used to compare each occupational pattern with the total commuter pattern.

The distribution of professionals and managers, the two generally higher-income occupational groups, is shown on maps (Figures V–4 and V–6), graphs (Figures V–5 and V–7), and Table V–2. The visual impression of a relatively dispersed commuting pattern is borne out by the tables and graphs, which indicate somewhat lower percentages of commuters within the four-mile zone. The managers, however, are clearly less dispersed than the professionals and the technicians. In fact, the distance profile for managers is quite similar to that for the total. The professional workers show a number of important divergences from the total. There is a lower proportion of professionals within six miles, a higher proportion beyond six miles. There is a low proportion of professionals commuting from the city, a high proportion commuting long distances from non-adjacent suburbs. The percentages for non-adjacent suburbs are higher for both professionals and managers than for any other group. There is little evidence of clustering on the part of the professional workers. Commuters are widely dispersed both on the city and suburban side. The managers,

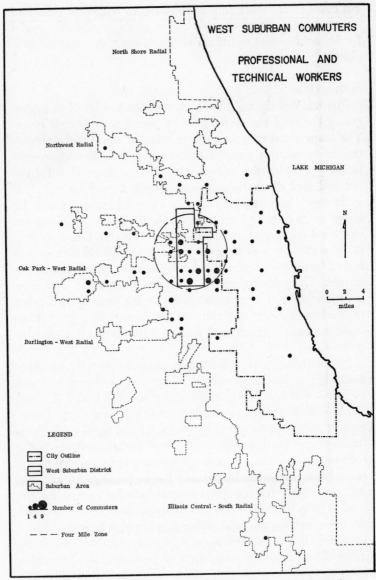

West Suburban Commuters—Professional and Technical Workers

Figure V–4

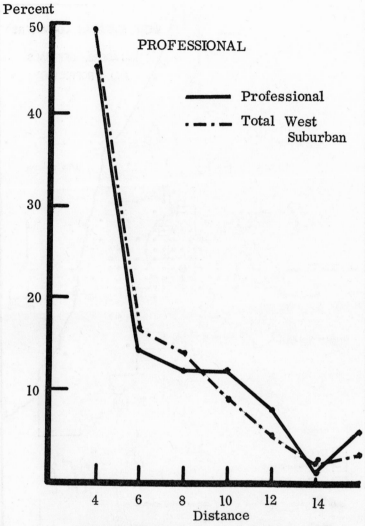

Distance Profiles—Professional and Technical
Figure V–5

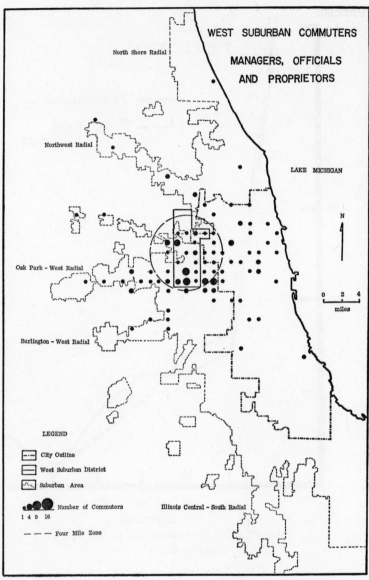

West Suburban Commuters—Managers, Officials, and Proprietors
Figure V–6

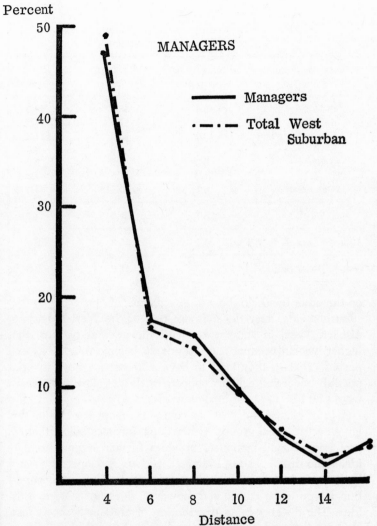

Distance Profiles—Managers, Officials, and Proprietors

Figure V–7

TABLE V–2

WEST SUBURBAN COMMUTERS BY DISTANCE BANDS

PROFESSIONALS AND MANAGERS

Distance Band (miles)	Professionals (per cent)	Managers (per cent)	Total (per cent)
0– 4	45.1	46.9	48.9
4– 6	14.7	17.4	16.7
6– 8	12.2	15.9	14.3
8–10	12.2	9.8	9.3
10–12	8.5	4.5	5.2
12–14	1.2	1.5	2.3
14 and over	6.1	3.7	3.3
City	28.1	31.9	32.2
Adjacent Suburb	56.1	55.3	58.0
Non-Adjacent Suburb	15.8	12.8	9.8

on the other hand, do show some evidence of clustering on the suburban side, near the southern part of the West Suburban district. Thus, in comparison with the general pattern, the higher-income occupational groups do behave roughly as expected. That is, they tend to have a longer journey-to-work, possibly reflecting a lesser concern with transport costs, than would be true of lower-income workers.

A brief glance ahead at the commuter maps for two of the large occupational groups with average incomes below that of professionals and managers provides further support to this idea. The distributions of clerical workers and operatives are both more clustered than is the total pattern. The next occupational type to be considered, however, does not support this idea. The distance-band distribution of craftsmen shows less clustering around the destination district than either of the two higher-income occupations (Table V–3, Figure V–8 and Figure V–9). Only 41 per cent of the craftsmen are to be found within the four-mile band, lowest figure of any of the occupational types. The distance profile shows further that the proportion of craftsmen is high between four and eight miles, but drops well below that for professionals and managers beyond 14 miles. The reason for this distribution may be seen on the map, Figure V–8, where a large number of commuter circles are lo-

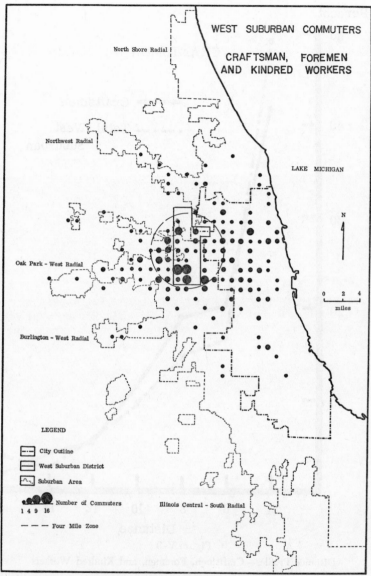

West Suburban Commuters—Craftsmen, Foremen, and Kindred Workers

Figure V–8

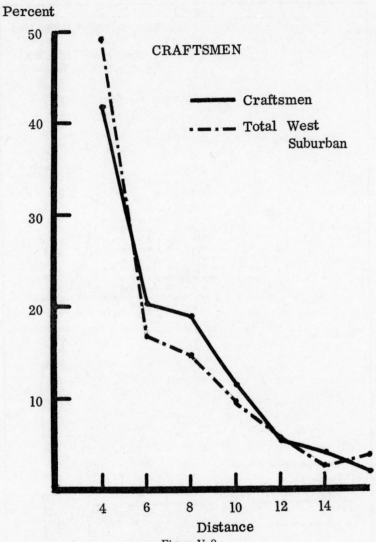

Figure V–9
Distance Profiles—Craftsmen, Foremen, and Kindred Workers

TABLE V–3

WEST SUBURBAN COMMUTERS BY DISTANCE BANDS
CRAFTSMEN

Distance Band (miles)	Craftsmen (per cent)	Total (per cent)
0– 4	40.7	48.9
4– 6	19.6	16.7
6– 8	18.2	14.3
8–10	10.9	9.3
10–12	5.0	5.2
12–14	3.9	2.3
14 and over	1.7	3.3
City	36.8	32.2
Adjacent Suburb	51.7	58.0
Non-Adjacent Suburb	11.5	9.8

cated inside the city. This emphasis on reverse commuting is further indicated by the fact that there is a higher percentage of craftsmen (37.5) commuting from the city than of any other occupational group.

Thus, the position of peripheral employment centers between city and suburb has meant less of a reduction in the average length of the journey-to-work of craftsmen than of higher-income occupations. The latter are more likely to live in suburbs, regardless of where they work, and thereby reduce their commuting distance appreciably, if they are employed at peripheral, as opposed to CBD centers. Workers such as craftsmen, however, are more likely to live in the city. For city-based commuters, distance differentials between peripheral and CBD employment centers are not great and are likely to be cancelled by greater time-costs of reverse commuting.

The next set of maps represents those occupational types which have shown the greatest amount of clustering (Figures V–10 through V–17). In both instances, the proportion of women is high. The component of the entire peripheral labor force showing the highest degree of concentration is the one shown on Figures V–16 and V–17, female operatives. Over two-thirds of these women are located within four miles of the center of the West Suburban district (Table V–4). Both maps and

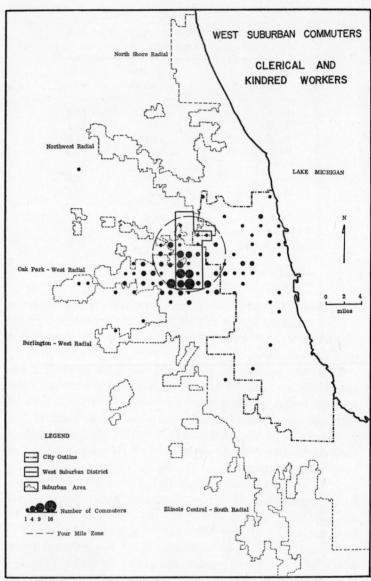

West Suburban Commuters—Clerical and Kindred Workers

Figure V–10

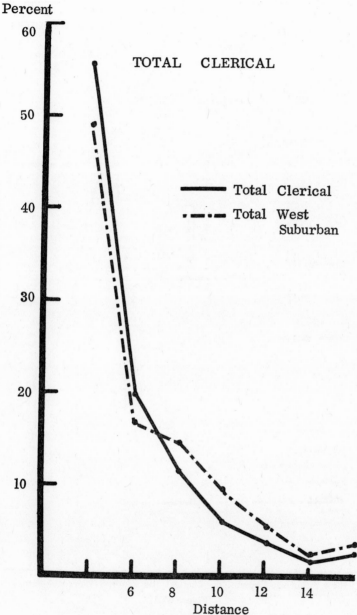

Distance Profiles—Clerical and Kindred Workers
Figure V–11

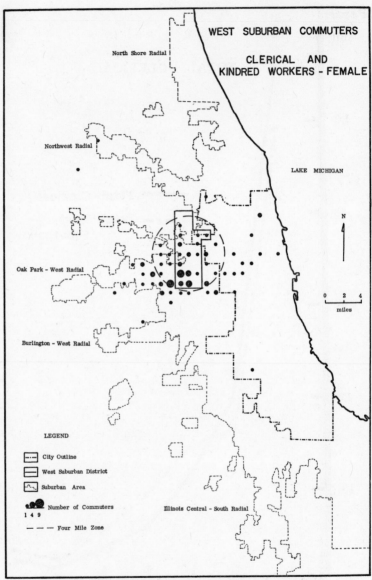

West Suburban Commuters—Clerical and Kindred Workers—Female

Figure V–12

Percent

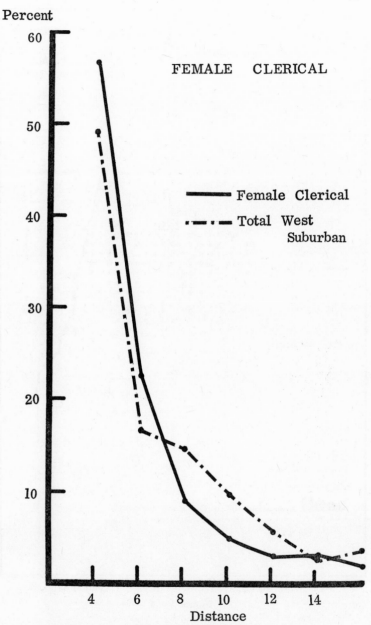

FEMALE CLERICAL

——— Female Clerical

.—.—. Total West
Suburban

Distance

Distance Profiles—Clerical and Kindred Workers—Female

Figure V–13

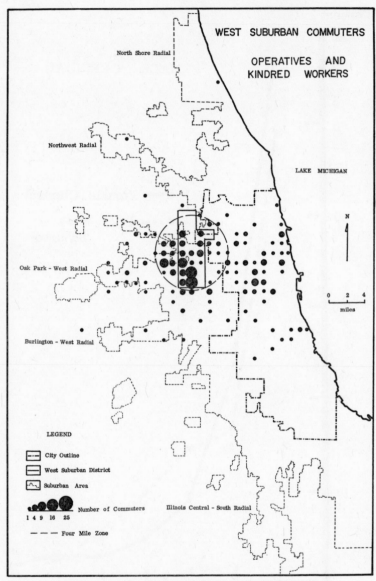

West Suburban Commuters—Operatives and Kindred Workers

Figure V-14

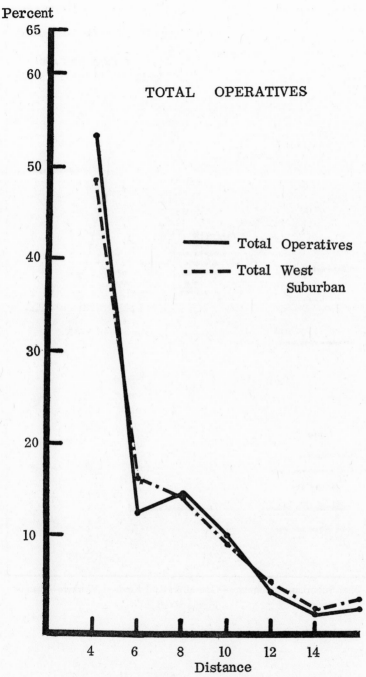

Distance Profiles—Operatives and Kindred Workers
Figure V–15

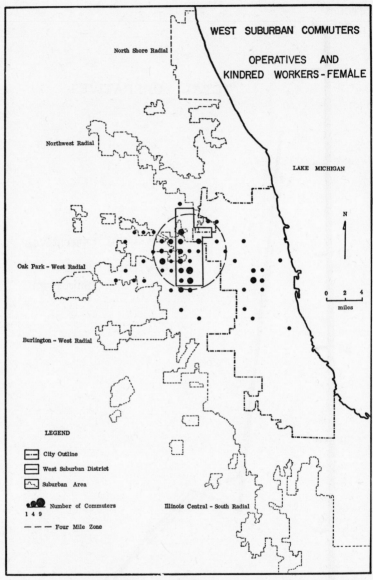

West Suburban Commuters—Operatives and Kindred Workers—Female
Figure V–16

Percent

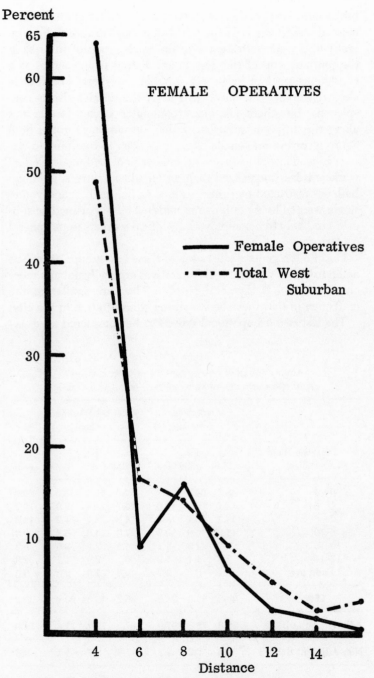

Distance Profiles—Operatives and Kindred Workers—Female
Figure V–17

tables indicate that the area of concentration for clerical workers and operatives is in the adjacent suburban radial. For operatives, the concentration is in the small group of suburbs at
the southern end of the destination district which serves as a
contiguous pool of relatively unskilled workers. For female
clerical workers, the southern end of the district also is con-
spicuous, but there are many commuter circles farther out
along the adjacent suburban radial, accounting for the high
figure recorded for female clerical workers in the four- to six-
mile zone. This indicates that the labor pool for female clerical
workers is less specialized than for female operatives, although
both are restricted by distance. That is, housewives and young
single women living at home in middle and upper-income suburbs are likely to be employed as clerical workers in peripheral
centers.

Despite the general clustering of these two groups, it will be
noted in Table V–4 that male operatives are really not any more
clustered than is the total pattern. They are similar to the
craftsmen in that they show a strong concentration in the city.

The last two occupational groups to be considered are serv-

TABLE V–4

WEST SUBURBAN COMMUTERS BY DISTANCE BANDS
OPERATIVES AND CLERICAL WORKERS—MALE AND FEMALE

Distance Band (miles)	Operatives (per cent)			Clerical Workers (per cent)			Total (per cent)
	Male	Fe-male	Total	Male	Fe-male	Total	
0– 4	48.3	64.4	53.7	54.5	56.4	55.6	48.9
4– 6	14.7	9.2	13.0	16.1	22.4	19.9	16.7
6– 8	14.3	16.1	14.9	14.8	8.7	11.2	14.3
8–10	11.9	6.9	10.2	7.3	4.8	5.8	9.3
10–12	5.2	2.3	4.1	4.4	2.9	3.5	5.2
12–14	2.2	1.1	1.9	0	2.9	1.7	2.3
14 and over	3.4	0	2.2	2.9	1.9	2.3	3.3
City	39.8	25.3	34.9	25.2	17.6	20.6	32.2
Adjacent Suburb	50.6	72.5	57.9	67.5	73.7	71.3	58.0
Non-Adjacent Suburb	9.6	2.2	7.2	7.3	8.7	8.1	9.8

ice workers and laborers (Figures V–18 through V–21 and Table V–5). These are lower income occupations and are not well represented in the West Suburban district. Although both are clustered as might be expected simply because of the income level, there are a number of ramifications which should be taken into account. The service group, Figures V–18 and V–19, shows a high degree of concentration inside the four-mile zone. Examination of the map indicates that this is due in part to the localized nature of service activities regardless of wage

TABLE V–5

WEST SUBURBAN COMMUTERS BY DISTANCE BANDS
SERVICE WORKERS AND LABORERS

Distance Band (miles)	Service (per cent)	Laborer (per cent)	Total (per cent)
0– 4	63.9	54.7	48.9
4– 6	18.9	10.7	16.7
6– 8	4.3	10.7	14.3
8–10	8.7	9.3	9.3
10–12	1.4	9.3	6.2
12–14	1.4	4.0	2.3
14 and over	1.4	1.3	3.3
City	26.1	34.7	32.2
Adjacent Suburb	69.6	56.0	58.0
Non-Adjacent Suburb	4.3	9.3	9.8

level. Local residence characterizes both owners and employees of barber shops, etc. The laborers are by no means as concentrated as the service employees. There seem to be two labor pools: one clustered at the southern end of the destination district, and one dispersed throughout the city, particularly in low-income and non-white areas.

Finally, Table V–6 shows the median-mile figures for all occupational groups, in order of descending income. There is noticeably less consistency in the relation between occupational types and commuting distance in the West Suburban labor force, than in the CBD labor force. In peripheral commuting, lower-income occupational groups such as craftsmen, laborers and male operatives do not have appreciably shorter commut-

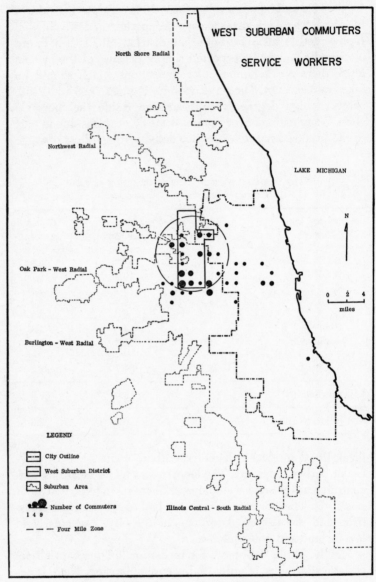

West Suburban Commuters—Service Workers

Figure V–18

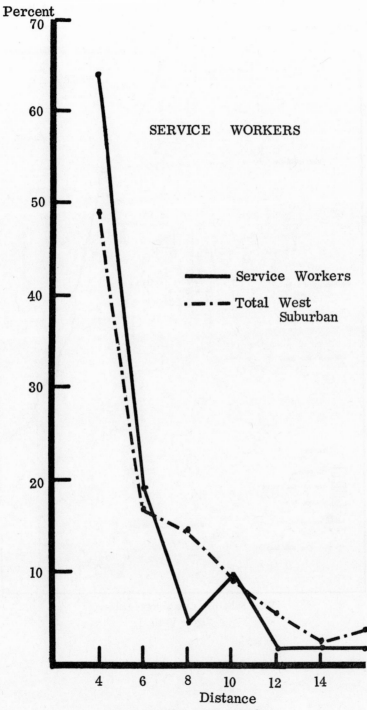

SERVICE WORKERS

——— Service Workers

—·—·— Total West
            Suburban

Distance Profiles—Service Workers

Figure V–19

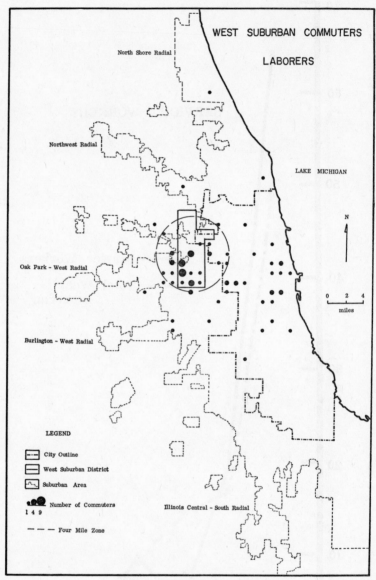

West Suburban Commuters—Laborers

Figure V–20

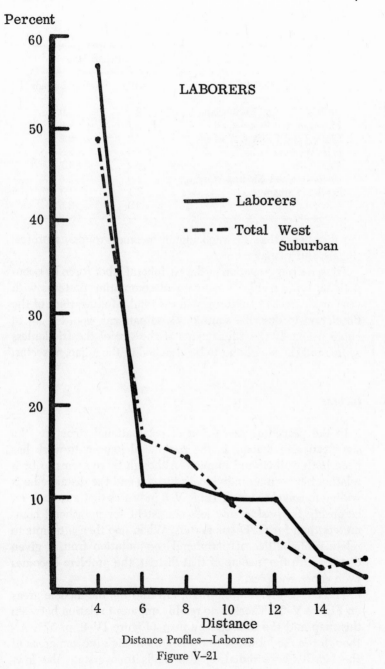

Distance Profiles—Laborers

Figure V–21

TABLE V–6

MEDIAN MILE COMPARISON

| | Median Mile | |
Occupational Group	CBD	West Suburban
Professionals and Technicians	8.5	3.9
Managers and Proprietors	8.7	4.0
Clerical and Kindred Workers	7.2	2.2
Sales Workers	7.6	2.8
Craftsmen	6.2	4.7
Operatives and Kindred Workers	4.9	3.0
Service Workers	5.1	1.4
Laborers	3.9	3.6

ing distances, than do such higher-income groups as professionals and managers.

Thus, a disaggregation of the peripheral labor force by occupational types results in component commuting patterns with varying degrees of conformity to the total. Modifications of the simulation to describe some of these patterns would seem to entail primarily the adjustments of the size of the frictionless zones, and the weighting to be attached to the adjacent sector.

Income

In the preceding discussion of occupational structure, the significance of income in the peripheral journey-to-work has been both explicit and implicit. Although there seems to be a relation between an individual's income and the distance he is willing to travel to work, Table V–6 indicates that any such relationship is considerably less consistent for peripheral commuters than for CBD commuters. When one then attempts to relate probabilities of peripheral commutation from a given district with the income of that district, the problem becomes even more complex.

The city is divided into high, low and middle-income areas on Figure V–22. There is no readily apparent relation between this map and the discrepancy map (Figure IV–8, p. 57). Although the model tends to overstate the high-income areas of the North Shore radial, it also tends to overstate the low-

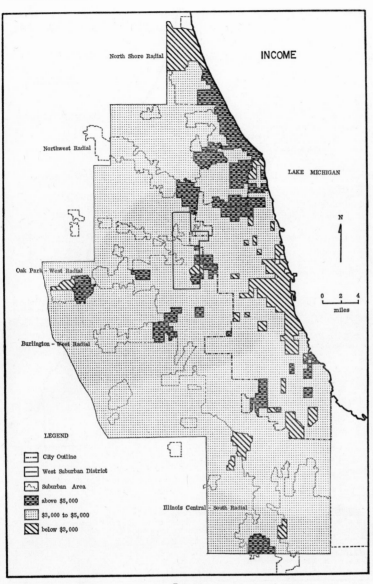

Income

Figure V–22

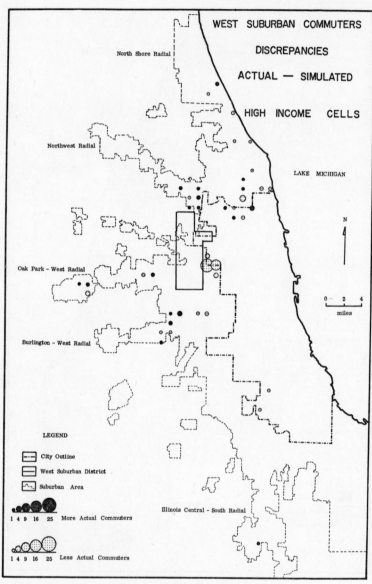

Discrepancies—High Income Cells
Figure V–23

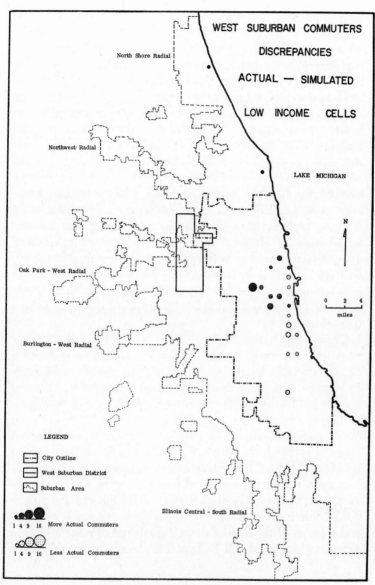

Discrepancies—Low Income Cells

Figure V–24

income areas of the South Side and the southern radials. A
closer look at the relation between the discrepancies and income is provided by Figures V–23 and V–24. On Figure V–23,
the discrepancies between actual and simulated commuters
have been plotted only for those square-mile cells which could
be classed as high-income cells on the basis of comparison with
census tract figures.[4] There is some indication of a negative relation to income in the presence of the light circles at the eastern margins of the destination district. These represent overstatements of the number of commuters expected from certain
adjacent high-income suburbs, as do the circles representing
overstatements in the North Shore radial. There are also, however, many small, dark circles representing understatements on
the same high-income map. The low-income map also presents
mixed evidence, although here, too, there is some suggestion of
a negative relationship in the presence of a few medium-sized,
dark circles on Chicago's West Side. These circles represent the
cells strung along Madison Street, however, where there is evidence of a strong sectoral orientation toward the West Suburban district.

Closer examination of the relation between the discrepancy
map and the median income for census tracts indicated:
(1) the overall relationship did not suggest enough consistency
to warrant further analysis; (2) there did seem to be some
income-linked differentiation between suburbs and their generation of more or less commuters than were simulated. Figure
V–25, therefore, shows Chicago's western and northwestern
suburbs as they have been categorized into five income groups
by Pierre de Vise.[5] It is interesting to note the diversity of pattern even within the restricted four-mile zone. On the southeast margin, there is both an upper (River Forest) and an upper-middle-income suburb (Oak Park); in the south and central portions of the district there is a mixture of middle-income
suburbs (Maywood and Bellwood in the south; Franklin Park

[4] These maps were constructed by: (1) allocating each square-mile
grid cell to a census tract by superimposition of the two maps; (2) clas-
sifying each cell as high, middle or low income according to the tract
classification; (3) plotting discrepancy circles on two separate maps, one
for high income and one for low income.

[5] Northeastern Illinois Metropolitan Area Planning Commission, *op.
cit.*, Map 9.

and Elmwood Park in the center), and lower-middle-income suburbs (Northlake, Melrose Park, and River Grove). Farther along the adjacent Oak Park–West radial, all suburbs are either upper or upper-middle-income.

The income diversity of this cluster of suburbs suggests the existence of a set of differentiated labor pools close to peripheral employment centers. A breakdown by occupation of West Suburban commuters from each of these suburbs illustrates something of the nature of these labor pools (Table V–7). Within the four-mile band the upper and upper-middle-income suburbs, River Forest and Oak Park, show a relative concentration on professionals and managers; the lower-middle-income suburbs (Melrose Park, River Grove, Northlake, and Schiller Park) show a relative concentration on craftsmen, operatives, and laborers. A third type of nearby suburb is exemplified by Franklin Park and Maywood. These are peripheral suburbs which seem to contain diversified labor supplies within their own boundaries. Both contain a considerable amount of local industry and have, therefore, attracted professionals and managers, in addition to the lower-income workers to be expected from their socio-economic rank. In addition, Maywood has a low-income section which provides 15 per cent of the West Suburban district's laborers. The diversity of these two suburbs, it might be added, is more apparent from the absolute magnitudes of the occupational groups than from Table V–7 which is based on percentages. Examination of the occupational figures for some of the other suburbs indicates that the female clerical workers are found in both the higher and lower-income suburbs. Elmhurst, although a high-ranking suburb provides a sizeable number of female clerical workers. These are the housewives and young single women living at home, referred to earlier.

Because of differing occupational structures, therefore, it would seem reasonable to expect higher-income suburbs to produce fewer peripheral commuters per capita than lower-income suburbs, since professionals and managers form a considerably smaller portion of the total work force than do craftsmen and operatives. The population-distance postulates of Model IV make no allowances for such differences between higher and lower-income suburbs. The model should, therefore, overstate the number of West Suburban commuters from

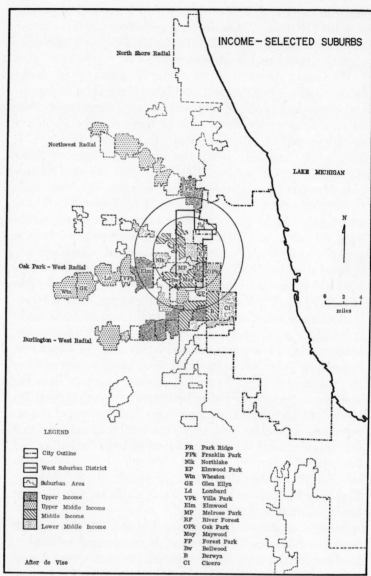

Income—Selected Suburbs
Figure V–25

TABLE V–7

WEST SUBURBAN COMMUTERS
Occupational Group by Suburb[a]
(Within Four-Mile Zone)

Suburb	Socio-[b] Economic Rank	PROFESSIONAL	MANAGERS	SALESMEN	CLERICAL	CRAFTSMEN	OPERATIVES	SERVICE	LABORER
River Forest	3	+	+						
Oak Park	24	+	+						
Elmwood Park	45			+				+	+
Franklin Park	48	+	+	+				+	
Maywood	51		+	+	+		(+)	+	+
Bellwood	55				+			+	+
River Grove	63			+	+			+	+
Melrose Park	65				(+)			+	(+)
Forest Park	67			+		+	+		
Schiller Park				+	+	+	+		
Northlake					+	+	+		

[a] A + under an occupational group represents a percentage at least 1.0 greater than the total percentage for that occupational group. A (+) means a percentage between 0.5 and 1.0 greater than the total percentage.

[b] As ranked by Pierre de Vise in A Social Geography of Metropolitan Chicago, Northeastern Illinois Metropolitan Area Planning Commission, June, 1960.

nearby higher-income suburbs, and understate the number from nearby lower-income suburbs. Figures V–26, and V–27, and Table V–8 indicate an irregular general tendency for this to be the case within the four-mile zone. The circles on the map represent net discrepancies between actual and simulated commuters for the suburban income groups represented on the map. Although there are exceptions, the progression is as expected. Within the four-mile distance band, Table V–8 indicates a slight deficit for the higher income suburbs, a slight surplus for the middle-income suburbs, and a marked surplus for

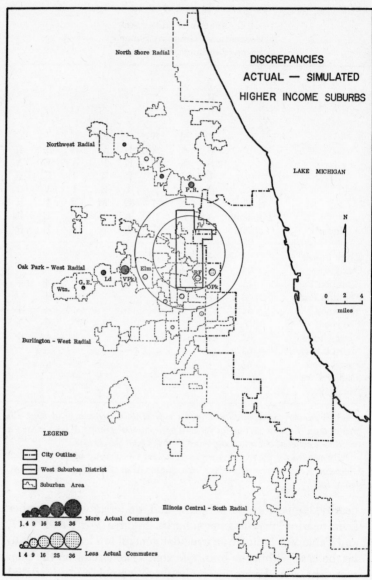

Discrepancies—Higher Income Suburbs
Figure V–26

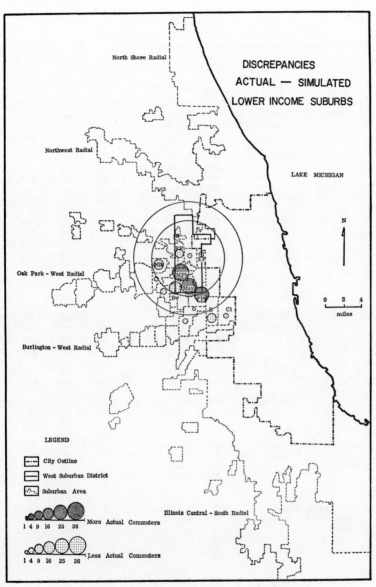

Discrepancies—Lower Income Suburbs

Figure V–27

TABLE V–8

ACTUAL AND SIMULATED COMMUTERS BY SUBURB[a]

Distance Band	Income Category	Socio-Economic Rank	Suburb	Actual Com-muters	Simu-lated Com-muters	Actual Minus Simu-lated
0–4 miles	Upper and upper middle	3	River Forest	12	16	−04
		24	Oak Park	38	43	−05
			Total	50	59	−09
	Middle	45	Elmwood Park	39	42	−03
		48	Franklin Park	52	44	+08
		51	Maywood	123	96	+27
		55	Bellwood	35	52	−17
			Total	249	234	+15
	Lower middle	63	River Grove	20	22	−02
		65	Melrose Park	71	41	+30
		67	Forest Park	30	05	+25
			Berkeley	06	08	−02
			Schiller Park	14	13	+01
			Northlake	25	37	−12
		72	Norridge	04	03	+01
			Total	170	129	+41
4–6 miles	Upper and upper middle	20	Elmhurst	27	30	−03
		29	Broadview	00	03	−03
		37	Westchester	00	02	−02
			Total	27	35	−08
	Middle	53	Berwyn	10	20	−10
			Total	10	20	−10
	Lower middle	66	Bensenville	04	04	00
			Hillside	13	17	−04
			Total	17	21	−04
6 or more miles (adjacent radial)	Upper and upper middle	12	Glen Ellyn	06	05	+01
		21	Wheaton	02	02	00
		30	Lombard	09	06	+03
		39	Villa Park	14	06	+08
			Total	31	19	+12
6 or more miles (non-adjacent radial)	Upper and upper middle	09	Park Ridge	07	03	+04
		11	Riverside	00	02	−02
		17	La Grange	05	06	−01
		23	Mt. Prospect	00	02	−02
		26	Arlington Heights	02	01	+01
		33	Des Plaines	03	01	+02
			Total	17	15	+02
6 or more miles (non-adjacent radial)	Middle	49	Brookfield	03	06	−03
			Total	03	06	−03
	Lower middle	62	Cicero	14	17	−03
			Total	14	17	−03

[a] *After de Vise*, A Social Geography of Chicago.

the lower-middle-income suburbs. The cluster of negative discrepancies noted earlier at the southwest corner of the destination district is probably associated with the higher-income suburbs to be found there. Beyond the four-mile zone, there is no consistent relationship between income and discrepancies between the expected and actual patterns. On the lower-income map, Figure V–27, there are few suburbs represented beyond the four-mile zone, indicating the total absence of West Suburban commuters from other lower-income suburban areas. Those that are on the map, such as Berwyn and Cicero, have fewer actual than simulated commuters. On the higher-income map, Figure V–27, a number of suburbs are represented, although only by a few commuters and by as many deficits as surpluses. There is an interesting string of low-magnitude surpluses along the Oak Park–West radial, however, which suggests that the strength of the adjacent-radial effect should also be considered as interactive with distance.

An examination of the effect of income thus has indicated a complex relationship to peripheral commuting. It is interlocked with distance, occupational structure and suburban location. Within a four-mile zone of a peripheral employment center, there is a negative relationship between income and per capita generation of peripheral commuters. Beyond that zone, any such relationship is difficult to detect. Many upper and upper-middle income areas and suburbs continue to generate a few professionals and managers but the lower-income areas frequently generate no workers at all. Modification of the model to account for income would be difficult. Higher-income cells in general might be assigned slightly reduced probabilities, and lower-income cells within the first zone might be assigned higher probabilities.

Alternate Employment Opportunities

As the examination of the peripheral commuter pattern has become progressively detailed, it has revealed more of the complex nature of the distance effect. It has become increasingly evident that the effects of distance on the journey-to-work often become meaningful when evaluated in combination with other factors. Even if time-costs were used, they would have different effects on different occupational groups. Alternate employment opportunities might be considered as another way of viewing the distance or time-cost effect. If, for example, a potential commuter were to be located at a distance of three miles from the West Suburban district, the probability of his commuting to the district would be greater, if there were no other employment centers within six miles, than if there were another employment center within one mile. In the peripheral traverse in Chapter III, the proximity of the massive Calumet industrial district noticeably affected the laborshed pattern of the Southern district (Figure III–4D, following p. 26). The distance to a given employment center should, therefore, be considered in the context of the distribution of alternate employment opportunities throughout the area.

Since the West Suburban district is an important peripheral manufacturing area, the distribution of manufacturing was chosen to represent the distribution of employment opportunities. The distribution of one-quarter mile cells which contain at least 500,000 square feet of manufacturing floor-space is shown on Figure V–28. This amount of floor-space represents a high manufacturing density and presumably a high concentration of employment. The manufacturing importance of the West Suburban district is evident. There are only a few other areas in the peripheral zone containing cells which have attained comparable densities, and there are no such cells in suburban areas farther out along any of the northern or western radials. On the city side of the West Suburban district, however, there is almost a solid wall of cells with high manufacturing density. The heavy black line on the map represents a dividing line between those cells which are closer to one of the manufacturing cells in the West Suburban district than to any other manufacturing cells, and those cells which are closer to one or more of the other cells.

Figure V–28 suggests reasons for some of the adjustments found necessary in the distance relations built into the earlier Monte Carlo models. The necessity to assign different distance functions to the city and suburban side of the destination district is probably associated in part with the proximity of alternate employment opportunities. The resemblance of the higher probability zone, on the basis of alternate opportunities

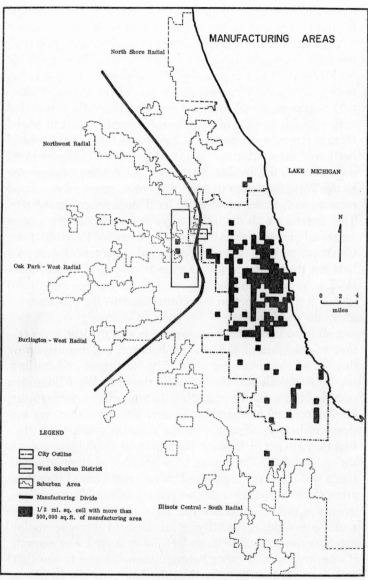

Manufacturing Areas
Figure V–28

for manufacturing employment, to the higher probability zone for the adjacent suburban radials is also noticeable.

Thus, in part, the effects of alternate employment opportunities have been subsumed into the distance effect, as modified for Model IV. There are also evidences in the discrepancies between simulated and actual commuters of the effects of alternate employment opportunities over and above those included in the model. An area of considerable overstatement in Model IV is in the adjacent portion of the city just east of the central portion of the destination district. Comparison of Figure IV–6, page 54, with the dividing line shows that despite its proximity to the West Suburban district, this entire group of simulated commuters is closer to alternate local employment in the city. This, together with the use of a geometric rather than a more southernly manufacturing center of gravity for the district, accounts for perhaps the largest and most consistent discrepancy between the two maps (See Figure IV–6, page 54, and Figure IV–7, page 55). The low figures noted for Berwyn and Cicero in the preceding section are also related to the proximity of alternate employment.

A differentiated transport surface is also evident upon further examination of the relation between the manufacturing divide and the commuter maps. The Northwest and Burlington-West radials are theoretically closer to West Suburban manufacturing employment than to any other manufacturing employment of comparable density. Yet, they show no evidence of being understated in the simulation despite the fact that they are not included in the high-probability adjacent sector of Model IV. The reason, of course, is that commuter railroads and relatively high speed radial connections bring these areas closer to the CBD in time-costs than would be expected, in view of their distance. This indicates that operationally more realistic methods of quantifying proximity to alternate employment are needed before it can be fully evaluated. For example, if one were to plot ratios between time-distance to the CBD and draw contour lines for the suburban area, the Northwest and Burlington-West radials would show higher figures than would areas within the adjacent sector, thereby indicating increased relative proximity of alternate employment opportunities. The same reasoning might apply to a string of positive discrepancies in square mile cells, which extend along the adjacent radial into the city. These cells are centered on Madison Street and represent an alignment of high West Suburban orientation. In part, this is due to the good radial transportation, which reduces the distance handicap of West Suburban employment centers vis-a-vis either the CBD or local centers.

The impact of alternate employment on the probability of peripheral commuting also varies with occupation. The maps for female operatives, Figure V–16, page 80, and for craftsmen, Figure V–8, page 71, provide a contrast in this respect. Few female operatives commute to the West Suburban district from the city side of the manufacturing divide. The craftsmen, on the other hand, seem less sensitive to the proximity of alternate employment opportunities. They show some concentration as noted earlier but also show a dispersion throughout the city in areas much closer to a number of high-density cells than to the destination district. This same tendency is, of course, still more noticeable in more specialized and highly paid occupations, such as professionals and managers.

Modification of Model IV to encompass the effects of alternate employment opportunity would be quite difficult, since some of the effects are already subsumed into the higher suburban and adjacent suburban probabilities. Some operational method of evaluating the degree of CBD competition, as reflected in a differentiated transport surface would also be needed in order to evaluate realistically the effects of such opportunities on peripheral laborsheds.

Summary

Thus, a closer examination of the peripheral commuting pattern and the simulation pattern has provided a number of additional conclusions. Disaggregation of the labor force by sex, race and occupation indicates: a clustering of the female labor force; a sporadic spatially restricted distribution of the nonwhite labor force; a weaker tendency for an inverse relationship between income and length of journey-to-work than is true of CBD commuting. Consideration of reasons behind the population-distance-suburban postulates of the Monte Carlo model indicates a complex intertwining of income and alternate employment opportunities with distance, which varies between occupational types. Although income itself shows no consistent relationship to commuting, probabilities for the generation of West Suburban Commuters are usually high for lower income suburbs within the four-mile zone. The probabilities for lower income suburbs drop off sharply beyond four miles. Higher-income suburbs, on the other hand, show lower probabilities within the band than would be expected from population and distance, but the probabilities do not drop off sharply beyond the four-mile zone, particularly for higher-income suburbs along the adjacent radial. The economically heterogeneous cluster of nearby suburbs forms a diverse, well-differentiated labor pool surrounding and including the employment centers of the West Suburban district. The existence of alternate employment opportunities helps to explain why it was so necessary to weight suburbs, particularly adjacent suburbs, so heavily in Model IV, since the manufacturing employment divide effectively separates city and western suburb areas. Further examination of alternate employment opportunities as a factor indicates that it is closely related to transportation differentation, and that it varies in its relevance as occupations vary. It is most pertinent in helping to isolate reasons for the clustering of female operatives; least relevant for the more dispersed workers whose skills and income are both at a higher level.

CHAPTER VI

Conclusions and Future Development

An examination of the journey-to-work to one of Chicago's peripheral areas has resulted in a number of conclusions as to the essential nature of the peripheral journey-to-work as a component of the aggregate metropolitan traffic pattern. In the first part of this chapter these conclusions are discussed; in the second part, some of their implications for the future development of peripheral commuting are considered.

Conclusions

IMPORTANCE OF THE PRIVATE AUTO

One of the most important findings is the degree of dominance of the private auto in peripheral commuting. The fact that more than 80 per cent of the West Suburban commuters use private autos, as opposed to 30 per cent of the CBD commuters lends support to the idea that the present structure of mass transit facilities is ill-adapted to the needs of the peripheral commuter. This overwhelming dominance of the private auto is a basic fact which underlies many of the contrasts between CBD and peripheral commuting patterns. The relative scarcity of female workers and non-white workers in the West Suburban sample and the Route 128 studies is, in part, related to the dominance of the private auto in peripheral commuting. The proportion of women auto drivers in the West Suburban sample is one-third that of the men. Nearly half of the women are auto passengers, and disproportionately large numbers of them walk to work, or use the bus.

THE TENDENCY TO CLUSTER

The average distance traveled by peripheral commuters is significantly less than that traveled by CBD commuters. The distance profiles show a particularly striking contrast. The peripheral curve drops off steeply for a peak in the first mile; the CBD curve rises from a low in the first mile to a high between four and nine miles from the center. Disaggregation of the total peripheral commuting pattern by type of commuter reveals that the total distance profile masks certain significantly different component profiles. The male-female contrast is quite marked among peripheral commuters, slight among CBD commuters. The median mile figure for women commuters to the West Suburban district is under two miles as compared to four miles for men. Because of the greater differentiation in mode of travel between male and female CBD commuters, there is less tendency for a clustering of female workers.

There is an important difference between the periphery and the CBD in the relation between occupational groups and length of journey-to-work. Among CBD commuters, the relation to income level is fairly consistent. There is a gradation from professionals and managers down to laborers in median-mile figures. This tendency has been noted in the New York study and in a number of other urban studies. It has been ascribed to the greater willingness of the higher-income workers to incur additional travel costs in order to gain amenities in relatively distant low-density suburbs. Lower-income workers lose in amenities, but gain in travel time by living in the city, presumably closer to their place of employment. Among the peripheral commuters, the relationship between income and journey-to-work is by no means so apparent. Although professionals and managers do register higher median-mile figures than clerical workers and female operatives, craftsmen, laborers, and male operatives do not fit into a regular progression. The position of peripheral centers on the edge of the city between the suburbs, where higher income workers live, and the city, where lower income workers live, results in a reduction of contrasts in commuting time between the two groups. This is not true with respect to female workers, however. Female operatives are the single most clustered group, and female clerical workers rank second.

THE MONTE CARLO POSTULATES

It was seen from the examination of a series of maps that the broad outlines of the total peripheral commuting pattern can be described initially in terms of population and distance relationships. A regression analysis indicated a weak, but significant relationship with an empirically derived distance exponent of one. Repeated modifications of a Monte Carlo model, based initially on the population and distance relationships suggested by the regression, resulted in a model which was used as the basis for simulating the distribution of some 1150 commuters. The model is based on the following assumptions: (1) a discontinuous distance function with a four-mile frictionless zone, a $\frac{P}{D}$ relationship between four and ten miles, and a $\frac{P}{2D}$ relationship beyond ten miles; (2) a doubled probability for all cells on the suburban side of the adjacent suburban radial; (3) a doubled probability for all suburban cells as opposed to city cells. The resultant map of simulated commuters could be regarded as a single sample of how a map of 1150 commuters might look if the only non-random processes shaping the pattern were the rules of the game established by the stated assumptions. Visual comparison and regression analysis indicate that the simulated map does provide a reasonable approximation of the actual map.

Essentially, the assumptions of Model IV indicated that, for a given destination district, the commuters from any cell are a function of the population of that cell, its distance, its position in an adjacent radial, and its location in the city or suburb. In equation form:

$$C_{ij} = f(P_i, D_{ij}, A_i, S_i)$$

where: C_{ij} = the number of commuters between origin cell i and a given destination district j

P_i = population at i

D_{ij} = distance between i and j

A_i = location of i in an adjacent suburban sector

S_i = location of i in suburban rather than city area

THE POPULATION AND DISTANCE FACTORS

Each of these factors may be examined more closely to learn how they affect the peripheral commuter pattern. In considering population, three ways have been noted in which population affects the probability of West Suburban commuters originating from a cell. First, of course, is magnitude. As was assumed in all the Monte Carlo models, the more people in a cell, the greater the probability of a commuter. For a given population size there is also some evidence of the importance of two other population characteristics: income and race. Even at first glance, however, it is obvious that each of the three ways in which population affects the distribution of peripheral commuters is tightly interlocked with distance. The effects of population magnitude, for instance, are postulated to be relatively independent of distance only within a four-mile frictionless zone, and to drop off at different rates in two zones thereafter. Income seems to be inversely related to per-capita commuter generation within four miles. Beyond four miles, there does not seem to be a consistent relationship, although both the highest and lowest income areas tend to be low in peripheral commuter generation. This spatial differentiation of income effects is due, in part, to the dominance of manufacturing in the West Suburban district. The very highest income groups are more likely to be CBD commuters and the probability of their West Suburban commuting is not greatly affected by distance. Some of the low-income groups such as female operatives are quite sensitive to distance. They show unusually high per-capita generation figures close to the district, and unusually low figures beyond. Racial patterns are also interlocked with distance as well as with income, and the nature of the employment center in question. Although the distribution of non-white commuters to the West Suburban district does not seem to reflect a sensitivity to distance, this sensitivity is implicit in the relatively small number of non-white employees in the area. As noted by Burtt and others, industries which depend on large amounts of the relatively unskilled labor associated with low-income non-white areas show little tendency to locate or relocate in the periphery.[1] The relative absence of the laborer occupational group from the West Suburban district is another evidence of this.

[1] Burtt, *Changing Labor Supply Characteristics Along Route 128*, pp. 15–16.

SUBURBAN LOCATION FACTORS

Distance, location on an adjacent suburban radial, and location in the suburb are also interrelated. All three might be regarded as expressions of transport costs and alternate employment opportunities. Distance in the Monte Carlo model is expressed in terms of circular zones, which implies an increase in transportation costs with distance over a sectorally undifferentiated transport surface. One reason underlying the increased commuting probability of suburban, as opposed to city cells, is the recognition of the lesser traffic congestion in the suburbs. At a given distance from the destination district, therefore, commuters from suburban cells will have lower time-costs than will commuters from city cells. A recognition of internal differentiation of the suburban transportation surface, itself, is implicit in the higher probabilities attached to cells in the adjacent suburban radials, where transport facilities are most effectively focused on the West Suburban district. The positive discrepancies along Madison Street indicate that the extensions of the radial into the city should probably also have been taken into account.

Alternate employment opportunities are also expressed through the distance factor and the two suburban-location factors. One of the reasons that the increasing distance from the West Suburban district reduces commuting probabilities is that it increases the relative attraction of competing employment centers. All other things being equal, the farther away a residential cell is from the district, the more likely it is to be closer to a local employment center, than to a West Suburban center. Examination of manufacturing densities in Chicago reveals, however, that other things are not equal in different directions, as a zoned or continuous distance function corrected for time-costs would imply. At a given distance from the West Suburban district, a city cell is more likely to be closer to a competitive local employment center than is a suburban center because of the large, absolute magnitudes of manufacturing still inside the city, and the scarcity of manufacturing in the suburbs, beyond the periphery. The presence of manufacturing in other parts of the periphery itself tends to bend the equal-distance line (Figure V–28, page 101) until it is clear that another reason for the high probabilities attached to the adjacent suburban sector is that it represents the center of a broad radial band within which the West Suburban district manufacturing cells have a maximum proximity advantage over other high-density manufacturing cells.

Thus, the distance, adjacent-suburban radial and city-suburb factors might all be expressed as functions of time-costs and alternate employment opportunities. It is probable, however, that the orientation of a suburban radial toward its adjacent peripheral center is still greater than one might expect in view of transport costs, and alternate employment opportunities. This radial orientation might be called sectoral inertia, or a neighborhood effect whereby the component parts of an adjacent radial are strongly oriented toward each other. The orientation toward the West Suburban district along Madison Street, for instance, probably exceeds that which would be expected on the basis of relative transport costs. This, of course, is related to Homer Hoyt's famed sector hypothesis which noted, in particular, the persistence of high rent sectors in the city.[2] It may also be related to a radial variation of what Torsten Hägerstrand refers to as a neighborhood effect.[3] In tracing the diffusion of an innovation, Hägerstrand observed the effects of person-to-person communication. That is, if one farmer in a particular area adopted a given agricultural innovation, his example or communication made it more likely that someone nearby would adopt the same idea. Thus, if someone in a given area were to be employed at a peripheral plant, it might be likely that a friend, or someone in his neighborhood knowing of his employment would seek work in the same plant. There is some evidence that such stimuli follow radial paths along major transport routes in urban areas. People who are moving to a suburb from the city tend to stay within the same sector; industries relocating tend to move out farther along the same sector. The net effect of such orientation would be to give rise to higher commuter probabilities from an adjacent sector,

---

[2] Homer Hoyt, "The Pattern of Movement of Residential Rental Neighborhoods," *The Structure and Growth of Residential Neighborhoods in American Cities* (Washington, D.C.: Federal Housing Administration, 1939), pp. 112–122.

[3] Hägerstrand, "On the Monte Carlo Simulation of Diffusion."

than would be expected on the basis of transport-cost differentials.

Another factor linked to suburban location is car ownership. One of the reasons for the higher probabilities attached to suburban rather than city location may be the higher suburban rate of car ownership. Car ownership, however, proved to be a difficult variable to interpret. It has often been cited as a key indicator for traffic generation, because it effectively summarizes income, distance, suburban location and, in the case of grouped data, population magnitudes.[4] Once these items have been accounted for, however, the interpretation of car ownership becomes more difficult. One must look for evidence that variations in car ownership for suburban areas of a given income level are related to variations in the per capita generation of peripheral commuters from a given distance band. Cursory comparison of the car-ownership figures with the Model IV discrepancies indicated no consistent relation.

RESTATEMENT OF BASIC RELATIONSHIP

Thus the population and suburban location postulates of the Monte Carlo model may have been acting as surrogate variables transmitting the effects of more logical variables, some of which are quite difficult to quantify in any meaningful fashion. The examination of other factors in relation to the discrepancies between actual and simulated patterns suggests that the postulates might be restated as: population magnitude, income, racial composition, time-costs, alternate employment opportunities, and sectoral inertia, or:

$$C_{ij} = f(P_i,\ T_{ij},\ I_i,\ R_i,\ E_i,\ a_i)$$

where: P_i = population magnitude in cell i
T_{ij} = transport costs
I_i = income
R_i = race
E_i = alternate employment opportunity
a_i = inertial effect in adjacent sector

[4] Among the studies in which car ownership has been an important factor are: Chicago Area Transportation Study, *op. cit.*, and J. F. Kain, "A Multiple Equation Model of Household Locational and Tripmaking Behavior," Memorandum RM–3086–FF (The Rand Corporation: April, 1962).

The first major complication is the fact that most of these are interrelated with distance. Since three distance zones were postulated in Model IV an amended statement could be:

$$\sum_{D=1}^{3} C_{ij} = f_{D_1}(P_i, T_{ij}, I_i, R_i, E_i, a_i) + f_{D_2}(P_i, T_{ij}, I_i, R_i, E_i, a_i)$$

$$+ f_{D_3}(P_i, T_{ij}, I_i, R_i, E_i, a_i)$$

In this statement, the variables are regarded as exerting different effects on total commutation in different distance zones. For example, low income will exert a positive effect only within the first distance zone; low income and high non-white percentages together will exert a negative effect beyond the first distance zone.

The above equations were partially operationalized as a multiple regression model, incorporating separate distance variables for each zone, and nominally scaled variables for the effects of alternate employment and low income within the four-mile zone. The results of tests made on a sample drawn from the West Suburban commuters must be regarded as inconclusive. Although the explained variation did increase from the previous 17 per cent to 40 per cent, the sporadic nature of the dichotomized variables and the fact that no allowances could be made for cells without commuters renders questionable any interpretation of the relative significance of the different factors, as expressed in their regression coefficients. One interesting result of the analysis, however, is that the variable for low income within four miles consistently tested as the most important single factor.

A second major complication is the fact that the total commuting pattern is an aggregated pattern composed of different commuting patterns for different occupational groups. As was demonstrated in Chapter V, some of these patterns differ markedly and the total pattern is greatly affected by the proportions of the different groups which it contains. For example, the reason that income seems to have an inverse relation to commuter generation, at least within the four-mile zone, is that there are more lower-wage workers than higher-wage workers and they will tend to come from lower-middle-income areas. Thus, there is a need for separate equations for each occupation, broken down by sex where necessary. For example, if there are n occupational-sex groupings which seem to affect laborshed patterns and m distinguishable distance zones, we might amend the earlier statements as follows:

$$\sum_{O=1}^{n} \sum_{D=1}^{m} C_{ij} = f_{D_1}^{O_1}(P_i, T_{ij}, I_i, R_i, E_i, a_i) + f_{D_1}^{O_2}(P_i, T_{ij}, I_i, R_i, E_i, a_i)$$

$$\cdots \cdots f_{D_m}^{O_n}(P_i, T_{ij}, I_i, R, E_i, a_i)$$

In this statement, the variables are regarded as exerting different effects on the commuting patterns for different occupational groups and for each distance zone within the occupational group.[5] High-income areas would have slightly higher probabilities for professionals and managers within a four-mile zone, lower probabilities for operatives and laborers. The effects of alternative employment opportunities would be most significant for female operatives, only moderate for craftsmen and male operatives, and least for professionals. The steepest drop-off with distance and the most restricted frictionless zone would be associated with female operatives; the next steepest, female clerical workers, who would also have a frictionless zone more restricted than Model IV, but less restricted than that of the female operatives. Professionals and craftsmen are examples of occupations which would show gradual declines in commuter generation with distance. A stronger emphasis on the adjacent sector would characterize the female clerical workers and female operatives. Race in the form of percentage of non-white population would probably exercise a positive effect on the laborer curve, a negative effect on the professional curve. The sporadic nature of many of these variables would result in many examples of specific factors with no effects in certain distance zones for certain occupational groups.

[5] It should be noted that the above statement has not been developed as a logically consistent theoretical expression. Rather, it is a shorthand expression combining some empirical findings with some intuitive suspicions, as to reasons for the patterns observed on the maps. Like many such empirically derived statements there are still redundancies. For instance, if more were known as to the relation between distance and time-costs it might be possible to use time-cost zones rather than distance zones and eliminate the time variable. For an interesting theoretical treatment of metropolitan transportation see Lowdon Wingo, Jr., *Transportation and Urban Land* (Washington: Resources for the Future, Inc., 1961).

Future Development of the Peripheral Commuting Pattern

A first step in the consideration of the future commuting pattern of the West Suburban district is to apply the postulates of Model IV to the anticipated 1980 population distribution. Figure VI-1 shows the 1956 simulated commuters grouped into two-mile square cells. It is at this level of spatial aggregation that the simulated commuters show a correlation of .92 with the actual, so that the map does provide a fair approximation of the actual distribution, with the qualifications noted in Chapter V. Figure VI-2 is a simulation based on the application of Model IV to the 1980 population map as predicted by the Chicago Area Transportation Survey.[6] The resultant map shows one example of what the distribution of West Suburban commuters would look like in 1980 if the population projection should prove accurate and if the postulates of Model IV should provide the basis for as good a description of the 1980 pattern as they did of the 1956 pattern.

The most striking feature of the 1980 simulation is the great spreading of commuters into the interstitial area. Commuters on the 1980 map are no longer confined to the suburban radials, but are diffused through the interstitial area. Virtually all of the interstitial two-mile square cells within the adjacent sector originate commuters as compared to just a few such cells in the 1956 simulation. One result of this change, as shown in Table VI-1, is to increase the suburban share of the total peripheral commuters from 65 to 73 per cent. Another interesting result shown on Table VI-1 is the slightly greater clustering within the four-mile zone. The projected centrifugal dispersion of population toward the suburbs will result in use of the vacant interstitial land now existing within four miles of the center of the West Suburban district. This would also have the effect of increasing the dependence of the district on the adjacent radial sector from 51 per cent to 60 per cent.

Obviously, Figure VI-2 should not be taken too seriously as a realistic prediction of the future distribution of West Suburban commuters. The number of specific local forces which

[6] Chicago Area Transportation Study, *Data Projections,* Volume II (Chicago: Chicago Area Transportation Study, July, 1960), pp. 27–30.

TABLE VI–1

1956 AND 1980 COMPARISON OF WEST SUBURBAN COMMUTERS
(TWO-MILE SQUARE CELLS)[a]

Distance Band (miles)	Actual 1956 Commuters (per cent)	Simulated 1956 Commuters (per cent)	Simulated 1980 Commuters (per cent)
0– 4	48.1	48.0	50.1
4– 6	20.0	21.7	18.1
6– 8	14.0	12.6	14.4
8–10	8.6	9.1	6.8
10–12	4.6	2.8	3.1
12–14	1.3	1.9	3.1
14 and over	3.4	3.9	4.4
City	34.8	33.4	27.0
Suburb	65.2	66.6	73.0
Adjacent Suburban Sector	51.4	50.2	59.7

[a] *Differences in percentage figures in earlier tables for 1956 figures are traceable to the use of two-mile square cells.*

affect the development of any single peripheral laborshed necessarily weakens the validity of any such detailed prediction. Granting the assumptions already discussed, however, the West Suburban extrapolation does suggest that a high degree of clustering and an emphasis upon adjacent suburban sectors will continue to characterize the commuting patterns of peripheral employment centers as population expands into interstitial areas. Once these general expectations for future peripheral commuting have been established, it is also useful to consider the possible effects of certain other factors. Changes in the nature of manufacturing, suburbanization or transportation development could profoundly alter the appearance of future peripheral laborsheds as typified by the 1980 map for the West Suburban district. No empirical evidence is available from this cross-sectional study. It should, however, prove useful to combine certain intuitive notions concerning peripheral commuting implicit in the study with scattered evidence from other studies, in a speculation as to the different effects on peripheral commuting of selected changes, in each of the following: the nature of manufacturing development; the nature

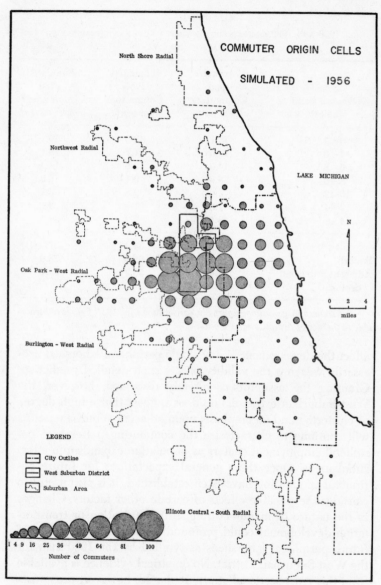

West Suburban Commuters—Simulated 1956—Two-Mile Square Cells

Figure VI–1

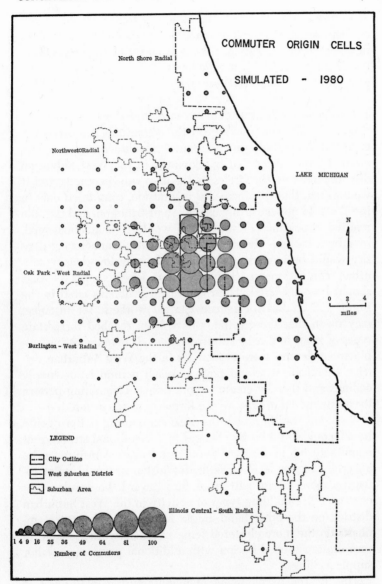

West Suburban Commuters—Simulated 1980—Two-Mile Square Cells

Figure VI–2

of suburban development; the nature of transportation development. No attempt will be made to incorporate these changes in a refined extrapolation. Rather, each set of changes will be discussed in terms of general effect which it might have on the pattern of peripheral commuting.

THE NATURE OF MANUFACTURING DEVELOPMENT

One change which will affect the commuting pattern is the expected magnitude of peripheral manufacturing employment. To the extent that employment in the West Suburban district increases, the circles on the map will become larger. It would seem that this increased magnitude, considered only in itself, would not cause any change in distribution, and that the relative importance of the circles would remain unchanged, save by a random element. The fact that manufacturing density would be increasing within a relatively low-density suburban context means, however, that labor supply ceilings should be considered. The recruitment problems cited in the Route 128 studies for female clerical workers, for instance, may mean that these ceilings have been reached for certain types of labor in nearby suburban areas. If manufacturing employment density were to increase in the West Suburban district, therefore, it would tend to reach certain labor supply ceilings and thereby create a more diffuse commuting pattern for occupational groups, which formerly were clustered.

A second way in which the 1980 commuting pattern could be affected would be by changes in occupational structure of manufacturing in the West Suburban district. A turn toward a generally higher level of skills, for instance, would point toward a more diffuse pattern. A turn toward the development of more office-building types of activity in the West Suburban district, on the other hand, might lead toward a greater emphasis on the more clustered female clerical workers—and, in turn, hasten their diffusion with additional pressure on labor supply ceilings.

Thirdly, the development of manufacturing in the rest of the Chicago Metropolitan area, will create a new set of alternate employment opportunities. On the city-side, this should make little difference since the divide has already been forced back into the district itself. The development of sizeable new employment centers along the Northwest, Oak Park–West, and Burlington-West radials would, however, alter the locational advantages of the West Suburban district for the radial and interstitial suburban areas, which are so prominent in Figure VI-2. The relative magnitude and the competitive wage structure of the employment centers in the West Suburban district would then determine the degree and nature of this effect. Although the New York study indicated little consistency of this sort in wage differentials, Burtt noted that new firms in the Route 128 area seemed to be paying higher wages than were older firms.[7]

THE NATURE OF SUBURBAN DEVELOPMENT

The type of suburban development which will have occurred by 1980 will also affect the pattern shown in Figure VI-2. In particular, the income and density of new suburban developments will affect the pattern. Low-income and high-density suburban developments within the West Suburban district laborshed would, in themselves, tend to increase or maintain the present marked clustering of the labor force.

There are certain implications in the occupational findings as to these future income and density characteristics which warrant closer consideration. As discussed in Chapter V, the location of peripheral employment centers between city and suburb has reduced the contrast in commuting time between higher-wage and lower-wage workers. Many of the lower-middle-income workers, such as craftsmen and male operatives, are scattered throughout the city. Their travel time is, therefore, as great or greater than that of the higher-wage professionals and managers, more of whom live in the suburbs. Thus, as discussed earlier, the usual pattern of the low amenity level being partially compensated for by low travel costs, does not apply. Relative to higher wage groups, these workers would seem to have been disadvantaged by the shifting of industry into the periphery, assuming that the contrasts in amenity levels remain the same. They would therefore be considerably more likely to move to the suburbs. They either would want to move to a suburb close to the peripheral employment center in order to raise their own amenity level and reduce

[7] Hoover and Vernon, *op. cit.*, p. 49; Burtt, *Changing Labor Supply Characteristics Along Route 128*, p. 17.

travel costs, or they would move to a suburb with equal travel time, but a higher amenity level. This would mean a tendency toward the accelerated development of lower-income working-man's suburbs, probably within interstitial areas. It should also mean an increased demand for housing in the overlapping laborsheds of the peripheral employment centers, thereby creating a rent ridge around the edge of the city. With respect to any one peripheral employment center, this might create a miniature CBD pattern for more distant suburbs. Land values would drop off from the center outward along both radial and interstitial sectors, although at different rates. Should these high land land values have the effect of increasing density, a pattern similar to the CBD pattern might re-establish itself with higher-income workers moving progressively farther out, again trading travel costs for the higher amenity level in low-density suburbs.[8] On the other hand, if densities should stay relatively low in peripheral centers, the lower-income suburbs will be forced farther out. The density gradient will then be much flatter than that for the CBD and there will be little tendency for commuting distance to vary directly with income.

In the New York case, the low-income, high-density labor pool seems to have developed, in part because of the existence of old cities within the inner ring of suburbs. It is interesting to note, that Hoover and Vernon cite the tendency for lower-income workers to leapfrog into low-income suburbs after a period of reverse commuting.[9] In the West Suburban case, there are no high-density, nearby labor pools in the form of old industrial cities. The evidence as to the possible development of these is mixed. On the one hand, there is the concentrated labor pool of lower-middle-income suburbs in or close to the West Suburban district. There is also a type of inner wave of suburbanization in the form of multi-family dwellings, such as town houses, which seems to be developing in some of the peripheral suburban areas. On the other hand, zoning controls in existing suburbs and the tendencies of most developers of

---

[8] For a theoretical discussion of this relation between land values and densities see William Alonso, "A Theory of the Urban Land Market," *Papers and Proceedings* of The Regional Science Association, Vol. VI, 1960, pp. 149–157.

[9] Hoover and Vernon, *op. cit.*, p. 213.

lower-middle-income suburbs, to express increased density in the form of small, closely-spaced single-family homes rather than apartment buildings, indicates the development of a considerably flatter density gradient, with a concomitantly greater dispersion of lower-wage workers.

The effects of any suburban density change on the present relatively compact laborsheds for peripheral centers, however, must be considered in the context of certain other changes. More specifically, the ratios between two sets of changes could be expected to affect the future degree of contiguity of the peripheral labor force: population density and manufacturing employment density; residential mobility and manufacturing employment mobility. If an increase in population density for the four-mile zone exceeds that of manufacturing density for the destination district, the commuter pattern should be more concentrated than on Figure VI-2; if an increase in population density is less than that of manufacturing employment density, the pattern should be less concentrated. The rapidity of the industrial migration to the periphery, together with residential-density control in built-up suburbs, would seem to point to a net pressure toward a greater dispersion of the peripheral labor force. The ratio between residential and employment mobility should also be considered. An increase in density may result, if workers move to a suburban area, in order to be closer to their places of employment. If many of them then change employment districts again, however, the result may be a diffused rather than concentrated commuting pattern. If people change residences more rapidly than they change jobs, the pattern should become more concentrated. If they change residences less rapidly than they change occupations, it should become less concentrated. The evidence to date is mixed. The evidence from Reinemann and from the Route 128 studies, indicated a sizeable lag between change of job and change of residence. Not many workers change residence when their firm is relocated. However, the 1961 Burtt study indicated that the importance of local-area labor for selected peripheral plants had in fact become more noticeable with time, both through relocation and increased replacement from local-area labor supplies.[10] One

[10] Burtt, *Changing Labor Supply Characteristics Along Route 128*.

might also expect relatively low employment mobility for the lower wage groups which form the largest segment of workers.

THE NATURE OF TRANSPORTATION DEVELOPMENT

Any attempt to evaluate the effects of the clustering of the peripheral labor force must ultimately be done with reference to the transportation system. It is clear from the evidence presented that the peripheral labor force is appreciably more clustered than the CBD labor force. This does not mean, however, that a shift in relative emphasis from the dispersed CBD pattern to the concentrated peripheral pattern will necessarily alleviate the metropolitan transportation problem. In the case of Chicago, the shift to peripheral districts means a shift away from 70 per cent dependence on high-capacity mass transit to a 9 per cent dependence. Despite the lower average length of the peripheral journey-to-work, the heavy use of the private auto may already be taxing the capacity of the highway system. Access streets in the vicinity of peripheral plants tend to become particularly congested.[11] People should be closer to work as more plants move to the periphery, but the effects of this on their commuting time-costs will depend on the nature of adjustments made in the transportation system.

Among the possible transportation developments are: primary and secondary peripheral highways, new mass-transit facilities, and secondary radial highways. Since 1956, a peripheral tollway, the Tri-State Tollway has been constructed, largely to the west of the destination district. Conceivably this could affect the importance of the adjacent radial as a West Suburban labor pool, by reducing its transport cost advantage over suburban sectors to the north and south. The 1980 commuter map would, therefore, show a greater emphasis on the Northwest and Burlington-West radials. In the Boston case, however, the peripheral highway has not had this effect. Burtt found that labor surpluses in one part of Route 128 did not readily flow into other sub-areas, and concluded that new

[11] James B. Kenyon, *Industrial Localization and Metropolitan Growth: The Paterson-Passaic District,* Department of Geography Research Paper No. 67 (Chicago: University of Chicago Press, 1960), pp. 179–180.

highways may modify, but do not eliminate the importance of the local-area labor supply.[12] An emphasis on the adjacent radial sector is not solely a function of transportation costs, but also of sectoral inertia and the distribution of alternate employment opportunities. Accelerated industrial development in the areas where the Northwest and Burlington-West radials intersect the peripheral zone would in itself have the effect of forcing a radial orientation on the future West Suburban laborshed.

The development of a mass-transit system or network of secondary radials, focused on the peripheral center, would be more closely adapted to existing commuter patterns. In view of the anticipated increase in importance of the interstitial areas, highways leading radially into the West Suburban district from that area could be expected to become more important. In this particular area, there are already some highways which could be classed as secondary radials. An important development for female employees would be the installation of more express bus services from a number of suburbs focused on peripheral employment centers along both secondary and primary radials. These developments would assume an increased concentration on the West Suburban district as opposed to other suburban employment centers. There is some evidence in Chicago and Boston, that there is greater concentration on certain portions of suburban areas for new manufacturing developments, as opposed to more diffuse growth of manufacturing districts.

Finally, the iterative nature of population and transportation development should be recognized. Any change in transportation facilities would cause variations in the population expectations set forth by the Chicago Area Transportation Study. Any population change would create a new set of demands for transportation facilities. Expectations as to the future thereby become subject to conditioning, by the direction of any significant initial change, be it population, transportation, or manufacturing, since each change may be expected to have multiple effects on this interdependent complex.

[12] Burtt, *Changing Labor Supply Characteristics Along Route 128,* p. 29.

Summary

This detailed examination of the journey-to-work to one of Chicago's peripheral employment centers, has thus revealed a peripheral commuting pattern marked by an overwhelming dominance of the automobile, a relative scarcity of female and unskilled labor, and a high degree of clustering of the labor force. The broad outlines of the peripheral laborshed are reasonably well described by a set of simple population, distance and suburban locational relationships. These relationships indicate that the effects of distance on commuting are discontinuous. There is a frictionless zone, within which distance has no noticeable effect on commuter travel, and there are subsequent outer zones of increasing frictional effect. Location in suburbs in general, and in an adjacent sector in particular, increases the probability of commutation to a given peripheral district. Commuting patterns at variance with these expectations are associated with certain other factors, such as: the presence of labor pools in the form of nearby low-income suburbs; the existence of alternate employment opportunity in nearby city areas, and the existence of sectoral inertia along the city-side of the adjacent radial. The total commuter pattern would seem to be made up of a number of distinct sub-patterns for different occupational groups. The traditional relation between income and distance travel for these groups is not as clear as in the CBD. Only female workers show a distinct tendency to cluster near the district, whereas both upper and lower-income groups of male workers show roughly similar dispersion patterns. However, higher-wage workers do show a greater relative concentration on the suburbs, lower-wage workers on the city.

An extrapolation of the observed basic relationships to 1980 indicates a similarly clustered commuter pattern with a greater emphasis on interstitial suburban areas, and an increase in the percentage of suburban commuters from approximately two-thirds to approximately three-fourths. Peripheral journey-to-work patterns will be further affected by changes in manufacturing, suburbanization and transportation development. Among the types of change which would reduce the tendency to cluster are: (1) accelerated industrial decentralization, which would cause manufacturing employment density within peripheral districts to increase more rapidly than residential density; (2) an increase in the level of skills and wages associated with peripheral industry; (3) development of an improved and less radially restricted transportation system; (4) the building up of interstitial areas more rapidly than expected, as lower-middle-income suburbs develop at progressively greater distances from peripheral employment centers. Among the changes which would accentuate the tendency to cluster are: a higher rate of residential mobility than employment mobility for lower-income groups; a continuance of emphasis on the adjacent radial sector because of inertia and the development of new peripheral employment centers; and an increased demand for female workers as office buildings decentralize. The net effect of these conflicting forces will probably be a somewhat more dispersed pattern.

In view of the present high degree of clustering, however, it is probable that appropriate transportation adjustments can keep pace with any anticipated increase in dispersion. Thus, it seems reasonable to expect that the continuing decentralization of industry to the peripheral zone may alleviate a part of the metropolitan transport problem by reducing the average time-cost of the journey-to-work. A vital question for further investigation concerns the nature of the appropriate transport adjustment. It is to be hoped that future research will provide a clearer understanding of the technical, economic and political feasibility of such peripherally-oriented transport facilities as secondary radials and peripherals, expanded bus services, improved internal access patterns, and a wide range of additional alternatives. Another promising research path suggested by this aggregative, cross-sectional study is the development of a dynamic model to trace peripheral commuting changes through time, at the level of individual commuter behavior. Finally, the recurrent references to wages, rent and transport costs in the attempts to interpret this empirical study indicate the need for recourse to theory in future study. A better knowledge of the explicit relation between wages, rent, transport cost and other urban phenomena would seem to be essential to an understanding of some of the reasons underlying these observed patterns of peripheral commuter behavior.